© BAREFACTS DIARY 1994

This is
PRIVATE!

KEEP OUT!

NOTES

DORIEN'S DIARY

by

DORIEN GREEN

Grateful thanks to Laurence Marks and Maurice Gran for putting my thoughts in order; to Lesley Joseph...oh and to my mother, where would she be without me.

First published in Great Britain in 1993 by
PAVILION BOOKS LIMITED
26 Upper Ground, London SE1 9PD
Text copyright © Laurence Marks and Maurice Gran 1993
Lesley Joseph photographs © Francis Loney 1993

Dorien's Diary is based on the character Dorien Green from the Alomo Productions Ltd/BBC TV series Birds of a Feather © Alomo Productions Ltd 1989

The moral right of the author has been asserted.

Designed by
Bridgewater Books/Peter Bridgewater and Suzie Hooper

A CIP catalogue record for this book is available from the British Library.

ISBN 1 85793 1467

Printed and bound in Great Britain by Butler and Tanner Ltd, Frome and London

4 6 8 10 9 7 5

This book may be ordered by post direct from the publisher. Please contact the Marketing Department. But try your bookshop first.

© BAREFACTS DIARY 1994

DORIEN'S DIARY

My Intimate Confessions

by

DORIEN GREEN

PAVILION

NOTES

© BAREFACTS DIARY 1994

Latin ...
Greek *dolikhos* long, Gothic ...
ingly *adv.*
indulgence (ɪn'dʌldʒəns) *n.* 1. the act of indulging or state of being indulgent. 2. a pleasure, habit, etc. indulged in; extravagance. 4. coats are an indulgence. 3. liberal or tolerant treatment. 4. something granted as a favour or privilege. 5. *R.C. Church.* a remission of the temporal punishment for sin after its guilt has been forgiven. 6. *Commerce.* an extension of time granted as a favour for payment of a debt or as fulfilment of some other obligation. 7. Also called: **Declaration of Indulgence.** a royal grant during the reigns of Charles II and James II of England ... giving Noncon... —in'dulge ...

INDULGENCE.

by

~~DORIEN GREEN~~

DAVINA VERTE

Pussy Golightly lay back in her sunken

marble bath, the exquisite scented foam

rising around her alabaster shoulders

like a cape of swan down. She inhaled

deeply of the heady scent "Lustvixen ",

the hundred dollars a bottle that had   *fragrance*

helped make her the world's leading

nouveau perfumier. And as Pablo, her

silent but attentive Catalonian masseur

-she often wondered how one mute from

birth could possess such a fluent tongue
when the language was the international
tongue of sexual ex^cess (that will do
MMMM soothed and smoothed the little
aches from her languid limbs, she let her
mind drif t. Could it really be only a
year since her husband Martin, the founder
of "Heavenly Scent Inc" had been murdered
by Amazonian tribesmen while searching
the Matto Grosso for new and rare ungents?
She squealed with delight as she was
suddenly brought back to the present by
Pablo, who had taken a deep breath,
plunged his head into the foaming bath-
water, and was now investigating Pussy
Golightly's very own Matto Grosso, for
who knew what.
"Enough of that" she snapped, hauling him
up by the ears. "Much as I adore your
slavish devotion, I have things to do
today that will not wait while I tarry
with you!"

And so saying, she stood up, magnificent,

flawless. Who would imagine it was the body

of a woman of nearly 36? Immediately Pablo

ran to fetch a huge Christian Dior towel ~~Ralph? Lauren!~~

ling robe of whitest Egyptian cotton and

wrapped her in it. Pussy strode across the

priceless Persian carpet into her opulent

bedroom. There, laid out on the hand built

Heals of London canopied four poster, were

her clothes. She was due to do lunch with

her merchant bankers, so the selection

had to be discreet. Her two faithful maids

Karen and Stacey, understood her needs

perfectly, The long weeks of training had

paid off.

As Pussy allowed Pablo to powder her all

over with silky talc from the Sex Goddess

range, she smiled to remember how hapless

the two coarse but well meaning cockney

sisters had been when first they had come

to work for her. Vulgar but grateful, for

had she not rescued them from a life of ∧

begging on the mean streets of

Edmonton?

While Pablo ministered to her body, she completed her make up. It took seconds. She still had the skin of a teenager, and needed very little in the way of cosmetics. Why try to improve on perfection, she always said. Her toilette complete, Pussy started to dress; slowly, sensuously, enjoying the feel of the rich fibres against her skin. First an ivory satin basque from Fredericks of Hollywood, then ten denier silk stockings by Christian Lacroix, palest coffee with the hint of a sheen. It amused her to know her under garments would drive any normal merchant banker wild. If only there were not covered by the austere but undeniably expensive classic Chanel suit she now shrugged on. Finally, the handmade lustrous calf leather stilettoes. There She looked at herself in the mirror.

If this was not the woman who was about

to persuade London's most cautious bankers *space*

to part with seventy million pounds for

her to expand her business, the she *n*

wanted to know who it was.

In the back of her chartreuse and cream

coloured Bentley Continental, Pussy

looked longingly at the neck of Kurt, her

muscular Austrian chauffeur, sexually

alert inside his tight black Jean Paul

Gaultier uniform. She wondered if there

was time to order him to pull the car over

come into the back, and indulge her sudden

need for a fast, furious, fantastic... But

no. She glanced at the little jewelled

chronometer on her wrist, thirty five £45,000??

thousand pounds from Horologie du Geneve,

a love token from Sultan Ibn Said of Oman

—or as she always thought of it "Oh, man!"

There just wasn't time.

The mahogany lined lift whispered her to

the penthouse director's suite of Abercrombie and Fortescue's City of London HQ.
There a uniformed flunky-in interestingly
tight breeches, she noted-ushered her
into a magnificent boardroom. It was empty.
Pussy sat at the gorgeous Hepplewhite
oaken board table, and opened her Gucci
briefcase. She removed her Mont Blanc
platinum nibbed fountain pen, her Smyth-
son's tan kangeroo hide organiser, her
gold plated Sony tape recorder-she kept
a verbatim record of every encounter,
business and pleasure-and her tiny but
powerful Okaynooki palm top computer.
She needed no lawyers or accountants to
help her close this deal. She was a
woman, alone, proud, capable.
The door opened. Pussy looked up. Her
eyes widened in surprise for standing
there was not old Mr Abercrombie. Instead
she was looking into the cool amused grey

yes of someone she had not seen for over

ten years. Her mind rushed back to a beach

in Barbados, a summer's night, the sweet

mell of Bougainvilleas, and the deep

American tones of one Leroy Barrington

whispering in her ear "Have you ever had a

threesome with a dolphin?"

Oh God!! Is this ↑
possible?
MUST do some research.
LONDON ZOO
071 997 6262

She snapped her mind back to the present.

eroy-tall, handsome, musxular, hung like   C

a bison Leroy-was speaking in his honeyed

South Carolina drawl. "Well Miss Pussy,

ow superb to meet you again after all

these years. Had you headr I'd joined   heard

Abercrombie's?" Pussy shook her head, for

nce lost for words.

"Okay" He continued "Let's get down to
business, and I'd appreciate it if you'd
stop undressing me with your eyes. "
Pussy knew nothing of that meeting. It was
as if the past, washing over her in huge
waves o f reminiscence, regret, longing and
belonging had wiped clean the slate of her
consciousness as the spring tide eradicates
a child's sandcastle. That or else too much
vintage Krug for breakfast. But no, Pussy
had never been one to let even the finest
wines fog her brain. No, it wasn't wine,
it was Leroy Barrington who had had this
effec t on her. As always, Damn him and his
 irresistable charm, his fifty thousand
 dollar smile, his dark pulsating man root..
The next sensation she was fully aware of was
the lustrous caress of softest leather on her
cheek. She opened her eyes, and was immediately disappointed to realise that she
was merely feeling the Bentley's buttery

hide upholstery on against her mouth,
and not the crotch of her chauffeurs
polished calf skin breeches. She pulled
herself into an upright position, and
fumbled in ~~her~~ the recesses of her Chanel
clutch bag for the tiny golden tape
recorder. She p^ressed the rewind button
and ~~listened~~ ~~to~~ as the tape whirred back
to it's beginning. What had she said or
done in Abercrombie and Fortescue's historic
headquarters? Pussy listened to the play-
back. What a relief! Despite Leroy's ~~di~~
dizzying prescence, it didn't sound as if
she'd given anything away! Her voice came
across as calm, determined, even amused,
although she'd never been on auto pilot.
(Let's face it, she thought, I've been
on most kinds of pilot in my time).

She listened, almost with admiration

continues ...

to her voice telling the merchant bankers
of her exciting plans to expand worldwide,
~~hoe~~ *how* the demand for her sensational natural
~~beauty range was growing every day,~~ and *the*
~~that the bank that turned down her request~~
~~on~~ *no,* demand, for seventy million would go
down in history alongside ~~xxx~~ the man who
turned doen the Beatles, and whoever it
was told the Wright Brothers if God h ad
meant us to fly he'd have given us the sort
of digestive systems that could cope with
in ~~fk~~ flight food. Her pulse raced as she
~~listened to her forceful presentation.~~
~~Surely they had agreed? She opened her~~
~~briefcase. Probably a cheque for the money~~
nestled in the suede lined recesses even
now? But then his voice came swimming like
honey and molasses out of the tiny speaker
of the tape recorder.

"A very pers uasive and exciting proposal,

Ms Golightly, or do you mind if I call
you Pussy? And one x**xx** which I can see
has my partners champing at the bit in
their impatience to invest in your business
dreams. But I feel a more prolonged and
private consideration of every aspect of
your corporate plan is required before
pen can be put to pape r. Shall we say my
place, eight p.m. tonight and perhaps you
ought to bring a toothbrush?"

As the Bentley turned into the sweep ing
carriage drive of x**xx** her Belgravia

mansion, Pussy c̶v̶oloured at the sound of
Leroy's a̶r̶rogant Southern tones. The man
had virtually propositioned her, before
~~the board of a seven hundred year old~~
~~merchant bank. The cheek of the man! And~~
~~she was still~~ fuming and fulminating at
his presumption as she threw a few flimsy
silk items into an overnight bag, stopped
only to add her new diaphragm and her
favourite handcuffs, and then hurried into
the dressing room, calling for Karen
and Stacey, to choose the clothes with
which she would, that night, close the
~~deal.~~
~~The two w̶u̶illing cockney servants bustled~~
in in their pigeon toed way.
"Yes Madam?"
"Something sensuous and easy to get off."
Pussy commanded, with a knowing smile.

INDULGENCE !

The Players:

1. PUSSY GOLIGHTLY

- Dallas type
- Power dresser
- No scruples
- Naturally beautiful
- Instinctively intelligent
- Huge appetites
- West coast body

(Based on me,
Dorien Green

2. KAREN & STACEY

Losers

(cont·····)

(cont...)

Flat chested
Bow - legged
Un- educated
Suburban

based on
Sharon & Tracey

3. MARTIN GOLIGHTLY

~~Dead~~   based on Marcus

4. LEROY BARRINGTON

forceful wheeler-dealer
Works hard & plays hard
Muscular, chiselled body
A rod of iron with a heart of
gold

based on ↗
Luke

S. PABLO - Silk-tongued
Anxious to please
Attentive to Pussy's _every_ need

Based on Troy

The Plot

* Pussy Golightly, world famous beauty and multi-talented, self-made billionaire from Chigwell, New York, revolutionizes the world perfume industry with her innate charm sex appeal & potent new smells.
* She is completely irresistible to all men.
* Boardroom & bedroom battles aplenty. LOTS of sex, shopping, film stars, nandos, a murder or two, leg waxes, kidnappings, holidays, sun, sea, sand, ski-ing, snow, calendars, condoms, fashion shows, paparazzi political scandals, champagne, caviar, jacuzzis, saunas, baby oil, leather, hand-cuffs... secret agents, fast cars, fast men & one woman who has the strength to create a world she could believe in.

A photo story by Doreen Green.

Oh God! there goes Melanie. She should NEVER be wearing THAT with her figure. Is she going to notice me....?

Hi Melanie! Just a few bits & pieces— Found

marcus's cards in his trousers. It was too good an opportunity to miss...

...Besides, I'm WORTH IT!!

JANUARY
M	T	W	T	F	S	S
31					1	2
3	4	5	6	7	8	9
10	11	12	13	14	15	16
17	18	19	20	21	22	23
24	25	26	27	28	29	30

FEBRUARY
M	T	W	T	F	S	S
	1	2	3	4	5	6
7	8	9	10	11	12	13
14	15	16	17	18	19	20
21	22	23	24	25	26	27
28						

MARCH
M	T	W	T	F	S	S
	1	2	3	4	5	6
	1	2	3	4		
5	6	7	8	9	10	11
12	13	14	15	16	17	18
19	20	21	22	23	24	25
26	27	28	29	30	31	

APRIL
M	T	W	T	F	S	S
				1	2	3
4	5	6	7	8	9	10
11	12	13	14	15	16	17
18	19	20	21	22	23	24
25	26	27	28	29	30	

MAY
M	T	W	T	F	S	S
31						1
2	3	4	5	6	7	8
9	10	11	12	13	14	15
16	17	18	19	20	21	22
23	24	25	26	27	28	29

JUNE
M	T	W	T	F	S	S
		1	2	3	4	5
6	7	8	9	10	11	12
13	14	15	16	17	18	19
20	21	22	23	24	25	26
27	28	29	30			

JULY
M	T	W	T	F	S	S
				1	2	3
4	5	6	7	8	9	10
11	12	13	14	15	16	17
18	19	20	21	22	23	24
25	26	27	28	29	30	31

AUGUST
M	T	W	T	F	S	S
1	2	3	4	5	6	7
8	9	10	11	12	13	14
15	16	17	18	19	20	21
22	23	24	25	26	27	28
29	30	31				

SEPTEMBER
M	T	W	T	F	S	S
			1	2	3	4
5	6	7	8	9	10	11
12	13	14	15	16	17	18
19	20	21	22	23	24	25
26	27	28	29	30		

OCTOBER
M	T	W	T	F	S	S
31					1	2
3	4	5	6	7	8	9
10	11	12	13	14	15	16
17	18	19	20	21	22	23
24	25	26	27	28	29	30

NOVEMBER
M	T	W	T	F	S	S
	1	2	3	4	5	6
7	8	9	10	11	12	13
14	15	16	17	18	19	20
21	22	23	24	25	26	27
28	29	30				

DECEMBER
M	T	W	T	F	S	S
			1	2	3	4
5	6	7	8	9	10	11
12	13	14	15	16	17	18
19	20	21	22	23	24	25
26	27	28	29	30	31	

CALENDAR 1993

JANUARY
M	T	W	T	F	S	S
				1	2	3
4	5	6	7	8	9	10
11	12	13	14	15	16	17
18	19	20	21	22	23	24
25	26	27	28	29	30	31

FEBRUARY
M	T	W	T	F	S	S
1	2	3	4	5	6	7
8	9	10	11	12	13	14
15	16	17	18	19	20	21
22	23	24	25	26	27	28

MARCH
M	T	W	T	F	S	S
1	2	3	4	5	6	7
8	9	10	11	12	13	14
15	16	17	18	19	20	21
22	23	24	25	26	27	28
29	30	31				

APRIL
M	T	W	T	F	S	S
			1	2	3	4
5	6	7	8	9	10	11
12	13	14	15	16	17	18
19	20	21	22	23	24	25
26	27	28	29	30		

MAY
M	T	W	T	F	S	S
31					1	2
3	4	5	6	7	8	9
10	11	12	13	14	15	16
17	18	19	20	21	22	23
24	25	26	27	28	29	30

JUNE
M	T	W	T	F	S	S
	1	2	3	4	5	6
7	8	9	10	11	12	13
14	15	16	17	18	19	20
21	22	23	24	25	26	27
28	29	30				

JULY
M	T	W	T	F	S	S
			1	2	3	4
5	6	7	8	9	10	11
12	13	14	15	16	17	18
19	20	21	22	23	24	25
26	27	28	29	30	31	

AUGUST
M	T	W	T	F	S	S
30	31					1
2	3	4	5	6	7	8
9	10	11	12	13	14	15
16	17	18	19	20	21	22
23	24	25	26	27	28	29

SEPTEMBER
M	T	W	T	F	S	S
		1	2	3	4	5
6	7	8	9	10	11	12
13	14	15	16	17	18	19
20	21	22	23	24	25	26
27	28	29	30			

OCTOBER
M	T	W	T	F	S	S
				1	2	3
4	5	6	7	8	9	10
11	12	13	14	15	16	17
18	19	20	21	22	23	24
25	26	27	28	29	30	31

NOVEMBER
M	T	W	T	F	S	S
1	2	3	4	5	6	7
8	9	10	11	12	13	14
15	16	17	18	19	20	21
22	23	24	25	26	27	28
29	30					

DECEMBER
M	T	W	T	F	S	S
		1	2	3	4	5
6	7	8	9	10	11	12
13	14	15	16	17	18	19
20	21	22	23	24	25	26
27	28	29	30	31		

CALENDAR 1995

JANUARY
M	T	W	T	F	S	S
30	31					
1	2	3	4	5	6	7
8	9	10	11	12	13	14
15	16	17	18	19	20	21
22	23	24	25	26	27	28

FEBRUARY
M	T	W	T	F	S	S
		1	2	3	4	5
6	7	8	9	10	11	12
13	14	15	16	17	18	19
20	21	22	23	24	25	26
27	28					

MARCH
M	T	W	T	F	S	S
		1	2	3	4	5
6	7	8	9	10	11	12
13	14	15	16	17	18	19
20	21	22	23	24	25	26
27	28	29	30	31		

APRIL
M	T	W	T	F	S	S
					1	2
3	4	5	6	7	8	9
10	11	12	13	14	15	16
17	18	19	20	21	22	23
24	25	26	27	28	29	30

MAY
M	T	W	T	F	S	S
1	2	3	4	5	6	7
8	9	10	11	12	13	14
15	16	17	18	19	20	21
22	23	24	25	26	27	28
29	30	31				

JUNE
M	T	W	T	F	S	S
			1	2	3	4
5	6	7	8	9	10	11
12	13	14	15	16	17	18
19	20	21	22	23	24	25
26	27	28	29	30		

JULY
M	T	W	T	F	S	S
31					1	2
3	4	5	6	7	8	9
10	11	12	13	14	15	16
17	18	19	20	21	22	23
24	25	26	27	28	29	30

AUGUST
M	T	W	T	F	S	S
	1	2	3	4	5	6
7	8	9	10	11	12	13
14	15	16	17	18	19	20
21	22	23	24	25	26	27
28	29	30	31			

SEPTEMBER
M	T	W	T	F	S	S
				1	2	3
4	5	6	7	8	9	10
11	12	13	14	15	16	17
18	19	20	21	22	23	24
25	26	27	28	29	30	

OCTOBER
M	T	W	T	F	S	S
30	31					1
2	3	4	5	6	7	8
9	10	11	12	13	14	15
16	17	18	19	20	21	22
23	24	25	26	27	28	29

NOVEMBER
M	T	W	T	F	S	S
		1	2	3	4	5
6	7	8	9	10	11	12
13	14	15	16	17	18	19
20	21	22	23	24	25	26
27	28	29	30			

DECEMBER
M	T	W	T	F	S	S
				1	2	3
4	5	6	7	8	9	10
11	12	13	14	15	16	17
18	19	20	21	22	23	24
25	26	27	28	29	30	31

PERSONAL

IF FOUND PLEASE RETURN TO

NAME DORIEN GREEN

ADDRESS BRYAN CLOSE, CHIGWELL, ESSEX

TEL NO 071 531 7697

PASSPORT NO 7310417   RENEWAL DATE 6/96

NATIONAL INSURANCE NUMBER How should I know??

BUSINESS

NAME

ADDRESS

must get a new one it's wearing out.

TEL NO

TELEX   FAX

MEDICAL/ACCIDENT

DOCTOR DR JACOBSON   TEL NO 0718SS 1321

NATIONAL HEALTH NO PRIVATE: B17992

BLOOD GROUP O

ESSENTIAL INFORMATION 36" 22" 36"

IN CASE OF ACCIDENT PLEASE NOTIFY

NAME MARCUS GREEN

ADDRESS as above - BUT PLEASE don't let him see this diary

TEL NO

BANK

NAME Moneylink   CODE NO 61-92-37

ADDRESS 10, High Street, Chigwell

TEL NO

CURRENT ACC NO 212167348

DEPOSIT ACC NO Marcus's acc no: 31274871

Marcus's PIN no: 1101

PERSONAL DETAILS

CAR

REGISTRATION NO **DG 69**   KEY NO

DRIVING LICENCE NO **1313770** AA/RAC NO **579316**

INSURANCE NO **???**

ADDRESS **— No idea — must ask Marcus.**

TEL NO

POLICY NO   RENEWAL DATE

STANDING ORDERS

DATE	PAYEE	AMOUNT
1st of month	} Allowance from Marcus	£12,500
14th of month	} Post House Motel — Standing reservation	£235.00
30th	— Andrew	£200.00
5th	— Gardening services	£175.00

CLOTHING

How do I begin? Favourites are:

Lagerfeld, Joseph, Browns, anything from Harrods, Armani, Balenciaga.

7.30pm MELANIE'S PARTY   FRIDAY 31

Invited to Melanie Fishman's for New Year's Eve Party. Somehow she got MARCO PIERRE WHITE to do the catering. I wonder what she did to obtain his services? — (I'm sure it's nothing she's never done before).

*New Year's Day
SAW IN 1994 * I got drunk on hot punch,   SATURDAY 1
Marcus got punched by a hot drunk & went home early. Made my New Year's resolutions :-
1) To be faithful to Marcus.
2) Never to spend more than £1500 on a single garment.
3) To help the underprivileged & mentally   SUNDAY 2
handicapped — like Sharon & Tracey — in that order.

Sun: Marcus complains his ulcer is rumbling. Why did I marry such a hypocondriac?? Because he was very rich & I was very poor— silly question.

£ £ £

                                          NOTES

Buy a Thank you card for Melanie

M T W T F S S | M T W T F S S | M T W T F S S
13 14 15 16 17 18 19 | 20 21 22 23 24 25 26 | 27 28 29 30 31

© BAREFACTS DIARY 1994

3 MONDAY New Years Day Holiday (UK and R. of Ireland)

Marcus in bed <u>all</u> day. Why does he never spend all day in bed with <u>ME</u>??! I phone his mother and tell her M's ulcer could be serious - she says he's always been a hypocodriac, I should ignore him. I make him lunch & go next door to see
S & T

4 TUESDAY Bank Holiday (Scotland)

I can't help noticing this incredible hunk mowing High Winsley's lawn. He smiles (!) His t-shirt is dripping sweat. I MUST NOT BREAK MY NEW YEAR'S RESOLUTION! He gives me his card - so why shouldn't I have a winter gardener as well?

ONALD
RVICES
idered
CHINGFORD
556 5454

DAY

Go to Harrods for the first day of the sale. It's chaos. Buy some interesting French underwear which has been reduced. If it was reduced much more there wouldn't be anything left of it!!

6 THURSDAY

No sign of S & T. Have they gone away?

JANUARY 1994

	M	T	W	T	F	S	S		M	T	W	T	F	S	S
	31					1	2		3	4	5	6	7	8	9

I had the most amazing dream FRIDAY 7
about me and MURDO - the gardener.
I was most defin'tely unfaithful to
Marcus .... _in_ spades .... _on_ spades ...
_in_ wheelbarrows - ENOUGH - but it
was only a dream and ~~that~~ doesn't
count.

* New French baker in the deli * SATURDAY 8
Oh my God! How am I
going to last until the
end of January? - let
alone _all_ of 1994 ???

Shopping List
- nail varnish
- caviar
- olives - stuffed
- bagels
- aspirin
- toilet paper

© BARF·

Marcus wants me to SUNDAY 9
drive him to Dr. Chomsky.
I do. There's nothing wrong with
him..... AGAIN! - He has nervous
bowel syndrome - CHARMING!

Dr Chomsky's clinic
081 716 7129

Harrods
KNIGHTSBRIDGE

RECEIPT

LINGERIE	£54.99
044532	£25.99
044533	£78.55
044675	£99.75
044676	£259.28
SUB TOTAL	
VAT @ 17.5%	
TOTAL	£259.28

THANK YOU FOR
YOUR CUSTOM

M	T	W	T	F	S	S		M	T	W	T	F	S	S		M	T	W
10	11	12	13	14	15	16		17	18	19	20	21	22	23		24	25	26

10 MONDAY

I telephone Murdo.
It turns out he does for Melanie.
Will he 'do' for me?
— He'll look at my garden on Sunday.

11 TUESDAY

Bump into Melanie in the deli.
She says Murdo's the best gardener
she's had. (when she says "had", does
she mean "had" or "had"??)

12 WEDNESDAY

Saw Sharon coming home from
work this afternoon.....
MY GOD SHE'S FAT!
How can a woman let herself get
into a state like that? No wonder she can't
get a man.

13 THURSDAY

*This is going to be my lucky
year!!*
Marcus has to go to Budapest on
Saturday — back in a week.

JANUARY 1994

M	T	W	T	F	S	S		M	T	W	T	F	S	S
31					1	2		3	4	5	6	7	8	9

M.

FRIDAY 14

If I buy lots of <u>indoor</u> plants perhaps Murdo can have a look at those for me. Its about time something grew in my bedroom. <u>OH! BUY 150 SOILED HOUSEPLANTS</u> — that should keep him busy.

✳ | MARCUS TO BUDAPEST | ✳ SATURDAY 15

Marcus is up at 6. When I say 'up', I mean...... Oh never mind!.... He kisses me goodbye and says he'll phone. With any luck I'll be unobtainable.

MURDO TO LOOK AT THE GARDEN ~~10·30~~ SUNDAY 16
11·00
I dress the way any suburban housewife would dress for a 15 stone gardener from Dundee who looks like Arnold Shwarzer- or whatever his name is. Murdo arrives at 11. I tell him I have some very sick houseplants. ~~He says he only works outside. In January??~~ I'm not dressed for outside.

NOTES

✳ DON'T FORGET
   THE PLANTS
   BEFORE
      SUNDAY

M	T	W	T	F	S	S		M	T	W
10	11	12	13	14	15	16		17	18	19

17 MONDAY — Murdo!!

I Break one of my New Year's resolutions.

18 TUESDAY

What a dish Murdo is! We've got quite a lot in common really — I'm into rubber — he's into rubber plants. he does work inside when pushed.... & boy did I PUSH — I've never done it in a gazebo in January.

19 WEDNESDAY

Murdo tells me Melanie is FRIGID. I love him even more!! He asks me if I've ever been to the KYLE OF LOCHALSH (?) — I can't wait!

20 THURSDAY

Pop in to S & T's this evening. Dying to tell them about Murdo but don't.

JANUARY 1994

M	T	W	T	F	S	S	M	T	W	T	F	S	S
31					1	2	3	4	5	6	7	8	9

Sharon wants me to go with her *FRIDAY 21*
to Harrods. Why not? Though I'm not for
people like Sharon getting too familiar
with places like Harrods. Its <u>not</u> Homebase.
I see this AMAZING fiorucci dress for <u>only</u>
£2750 (It was £5500) I break the second
of my New Year's resolutions - Sharon buys a
Harrods mug.

SATURDAY 22

Marcus phones - he's stuck in   MARCUS HOME
Budapest and won't be   FROM BUDAPEST
home until Tuesday - Pehaps I'll phone
Murdo and take him to the Highlands
tomorrow (?) He wears a kilt when he's in
Scotland — Never had a man in a kilt.

MURDO 11·00 am
SUNDAY 23

Tracey comes round this morning. I try
to get rid of her before Murdo arrives.
I give him a copy of 'My secret Garden'
by Nancy Friday - he thinks it's a gardening
book. BOY, IS HE IN FOR A SHOCK WHEN HE
READS IT !!

NOTES

Marcus
Budapest sheraton
461327
room no: 137

MURDO!

24 MONDAY

Murdo and I try to work out why my geraniums are not growing as they should be — Murdo says he doesn't have a problem with his..... This man is <u>NOT</u> kidding.

25 TUESDAY

Marcus due home today

— I don't know what time.

26 WEDNESDAY Marcus arrived around Australia Day midday and brought me a figurine from Hungary. I asked what he did in Budapest, he said I wouldn't understand. He asked what I did whilst he was away — I told him he wouldn't understand !!!

27   AY

M. asks why the house is full of house plants — Don't I know he suffers from Hay Fever?

ERANIUM

WARM AND SUNNY

KEEP MOIST

M	T	W	T	F	S	S		M	T	W	T	F	S	S
31					1	2		3	4	5	6	7	8	9

FRIDAY 28

M. offers to take me out to dinner in London, then starts sneezing violently & doesn't stop. I can't sleep with him when he's like this. Mind you — it's the nearest he ever comes to moving for more than 5 minutes.

SATURDAY 29

I telephone Murdo & suggest we go to Scotland on Wednesday and return for Sunday evening. My treat. He says he'd love me to see the Trossachs...

071 397 6173

SUNDAY 30

Tomorrow afternoon I have an appointment with my Harley St. doctor - Mr Salamone. Look into the possibilities of having my boobs enlarged.

NOTES

car hire?

booked flight BA 672 9:30 am to Inverness on 2.2.93

		W	T	F	S	S		M	T	W	T	F	S	S
		19	20	21	22	23		24	25	26	27	28	29	30

31 MONDAY Mr. Salamone says I'm too short to have a 40" bust & there's a fair chance I'd topple over. STUPID MAN! With a 40" bust I won't be on my feet that often. He asks what my husband thinks - I tell the good doctor he probably won't even notice. We lead separate lives. Then why do I want my boobs enlarged he asks? Because I want to be the

1 TUESDAY UK President of the Dolly Parton fan club. HONESTLY - how does a man like this become a cosmetic surgeon?

Tell Marcus I have to go into a 'women's only' clinic for exploratory tests tomorrow. He asks what time supper will be. I tell him I might be in overnight or two. He says he'll go to his mother's for supper.

2 WEDNESDAY FLY 9.30 A.M. I meet Murdo at Stansted & we fly to Inverness, then rent a car and drive to Loch Ness. We sit at the edge of the Loch and one thing leads to another..... Don't let anyone tell me there's no such thing as a Loch Ness Monster - I've seen it. I reached out & touched it !!!

3 THURSDAY

Murdo telephones Marcus and says he's a consultant and that everything is all right. "Dorien will be home on Sunday." Marcus asks if it will be lunch or dinner time? My husband is OBSESSED with food. His whole life revolves around meal times.

FEBRUARY 1994	M	T	W	T	F	S	S		M	T	W	T	F	S	S
			1	2	3	4	5	6	7	8	9	10	11	12	13

SCOTLAND

MURDO WEARS HIS KILT! How he *FRIDAY 4* doesn't catch a cold I don't know. I often wondered what scotsman wear under their kilts – the same thing I wear under my Armani skirt – ZILCH! It just makes getting there so easy.

SATURDAY 5

We take the lift to the top of Ben Nevis. At nearly 4500ft this is the <u>HIGHEST</u> position I've <u>EVER</u> <u>MADE IT</u> !! – we miss the last lift down.

RETURN FROM SCOTLAND *SUNDAY 6*

<u>OH MY GOD</u>! M. is expecting me home & we are stuck up Ben Nevis.
Murdo calms me down with those amazing biceps, pecs, & thighs of his. By midday we are down in Fort William & fly back to Stansted.

NOTES

© BAREFACTS DIARY 1994

M	T	W	T	F	S	S	M					S	S
14	15	16	17	18	19	20	21						

7 MONDAY I'm growing a little bored with Murdo. He _never_ wants to go indoors. Gazebo's, Lochs, up mountains, the Skye to Kyle of Lochalsh ferry.... yes! BUT _NEVER_ IN BED. Call me old fashioned, but there's something reassuring about going to sleep afterwards —NOT suffering from frostbite!

8 TUESDAY

Sharon & I go to a new wine bar in Abridge.
We get picked up by two 20 year olds— Baz and Gaz. Sharon disappears with Baz leaving me with 'Brain Rot of Britain'.

9 WEDNESDAY

* Hairdressers 9.30*
- Facial with Marie at 12.30.

10 THURSDAY

Marcus wants to go with me to Harley Street tomorrow. He found my appointment card whilst looking for his migraine tablets. He's worried and jealous. Worried something might be wrong with me, and jealous there's not something really wrong with him.

FEBRUARY 1994

M	T	W	T	F	S	S	M	T	W	T	F	S	S
1	2	3	4	5	6		7	8	9	10	11	12	13

DOCTOR SALAMONE 2.15pm

Persuade M. I'd rather go alone to Harley
Street. Dr. Salamone tells me that a boob
enlargement job is a long process & could
be dangerous. It is also very expensive
and only one in ten actually take.
—They've also been known to explode in
aeroplanes.

- Tracey's for morning coffee.
I try and explain about my intended
op — she keeps on about what is it?
I eventually tell her but SWEAR her to
secrecy. She says she wouldn't let
anyone mess with her "threepennies".
Sometimes she speaks another
language to normal Chigwell folk!

Mummy's 3.00

Visit mummy this afternoon.
GOD, Colindale is so depressing! How
did I ever live there for eighteen years???

*
collect flowers
for mummy
on saturday afternoon.

14 MONDAY 💙

💙 VALENTINE'S DAY 💙   — Get up before
💙   the post-
* Book manicure & pedicure man
for tomorrow afternoon.   arrives

(only 12 cards this year)

15 TUESDAY

- Marie 3.30 manicure etc.
  Spend the afternoon getting ready for
  M's Lodge do tomorrow — I don't know
  what to wear. Think about the Balenciaga
  and the Conran but they're both <u>so</u> boring.
  Sharon comes in and asks if I'd thought
  about 'Next'? — Where is this girl's head at?

16 WEDNESDAY M'S LODGE DO

Take a taxi to London and buy, on impulse,
a lovely little Lagerfeld dress. Try and
bait price down from £3500 but, because
I'm paying with Marcus's Amex card,
the salesman says he can't do anything
on the price. Still — it's only money.

17 THURSDAY Well, that's the <u>LAST</u> time I'm going
to one of M's Lodge affairs. The STUPID man
on my right threw up down my Lagerfeld!
What a <u>common</u> lot. — Pulled a very nice
         chiropodist — Denholm. Told
         him I'd been suffering from
         hard skin. He said if I
         wanted to see <u>HARD</u> skin

RING MUMMY

Go to Mummy's for supper - She has a new man. She says he's a professional man, but won't tell me which profession. Marcus can't come. Business in Southampton - I sometimes think he's got a lover....

Murdo phones completely out of the blue! Asks me if I want to go rock climbing with him. Is this a euphemism ???

6pm.... The Police call. Marcus has been in a road accident - the Jaguar is a write off. Thank God. It was only an 'f' reg. M. is in Southampton General suffering from slight concussion. The police offer to take me down to see him. I suppose I'd better go.

Southampton General
0703 722122
ward E6

081322
1114
110pm

	M	T	W	T	F	S	S		M	T	W	T	F	S	S
S									M	T	W	T	F	S	S
20	21	22	23	24	25	26	27		28						

21 MONDAY

Holiday Inn
0703-939739

WHAT A DEAD & ALIVE HOLE
SOUTHAMPTON IS.

Visit Marcus - he's all right.

Book into the Southampton
Holiday Inn

...SDAY

Get chatted up by a computer
rep called Alick. He tells me
this hard luck story of his
marriage. I tell him <u>all</u> about
Marcus & he feels sorry for me.
No, I didn't tell him Marcus was
in an accident - I just told him
about Marcus. We have a bottle
of champagne & spend the
night in his room. Nothing
happened - Alick was too drunk!

...AY

ICK HENDERSON
SALES REPRESENTATIVE

HCC Ltd
211 Beaufort Way
Southampton
Hants

Tel 0703 989898
Mobile 0833 433333

<u>Weds - Back to Chigwell</u>

---

24 THURSDAY <u>TENNIS 11·00</u> with Melanie

Melanie and I go to the tennis club - we
are down for Court 4 at 11am. Two
guys (not bad) ask if we would like a
mixed doubles - I play with Simon - he's
quite good. Married. Asks if I would like to
have lunch with him tomorrow. Melanie's
<u>FURIOUS</u> as her partner, Clive, is a GLOMP!

FEBRUARY 1994

M	T	W	T	F	S	S		M	T	W	T	F	S	S
	1	2	3	4	5	6		7	8	9	10	11	12	13

LUNCH WITH S. 1·00pm

Simon takes me to his flat for lunch — <u>Great cook</u>. He shows me his bedroom which is <u>very</u> strange — He's into bondage... MY KIND OF MAN!!

Went round to Simon's. Problem is I put the cuffs on him & mislaid the key. Still — his cleaning lady will be in at nine tomorrow — Perhaps she will know where he keeps a spare.

Buy some new tennis knickers

S.

28 MONDAY M. GOES AWAY

Marcus off for yet another of his business
trips. I suppose the air miles will come
in useful one day....
Went next door but found Tracey has become
addicted to Garth's computer games AND
has lost the art of conversation - not that
she was ever that good at it.

1 TUESDAY

Went shopping with Melanie Fishman -
God knows why - she's got longer legs
and better tits (though I'd never admit
it to her). Nothing worth buying in all
of Bond St. suggest we pop over to
Paris .....

2 WEDNESDAY

Woke up in an Emperor Louis Napoleon-
size bed in Hotel Guillon - makes the
Savoy look like the Basildon Post House.
IF ONLY... I hadn't woken up alone.
Croissants with Melanie then BLITZ
Rue St. Honore - spent 25000 francs -
must be losing my touch!!

3 THURSDAY

woke up in bed alone ..... AGAIN!! Briefly
wondered whether the 7,000 francs I
spent on lingerie had been wasted.
The the waiter came in. I hadn't
ordered a baguette so I know he was
pleased to see me!!!

MARCH 1994

M	T	W	T	F	S	S	M	T	W	T	F	S	S
		1	2	3	4	5	6	7	8	9	10	11	12	13

Jules, the obliging waiter, did NOT turn up with my breakfast. felt guilty at the thought he might have got the sack for spending ALL day in bed with me. Met Melanie for brunch, learned he spent ALL night in bed with her COW!!

* MUMMY'S BIRTHDAY *

Sent her a card and a BIG Interflora bunch of white lillies. They remind her of death. Went to synagogue because of sudden attack of Jewish guilt..... Well.... about EVERY-THING really.

WE'RE IN GSTAAD!! – winter playground of hyper-rich Euro Trash, two of whom, Marcel & Jerome picked us up at MAXIM'S yesterday. Check into PALACE HOTEL – and forced to spend 3000 S.F. on emergency ski-wear!

Interflora
681 2121

M	T	W	T	F	S	S		M	T	W	T	F	S	S		M	T	W	T	F
14	15	16	17	18	19	20		21	22	23	24	25	26	27		28	29	30	31	

M. AWAY

7 MONDAY

Marcel wakes me at 6am! I say "NO, Marcel, <u>not again</u>. Five times in one night is my limit in a new country." Turns out the idiot expects me to go ski-ing <u>just</u> because I bought the gear! The only part of ski-ing I like is feeling the bar of the ski-lift between my thighs!

8 TUESDAY

<u>Return to London</u> with... LEG IN PLASTER. Should never have let Marcel persuade me onto his two-man bob — and once on it I should certainly have NEVER let him do THAT! — At least its only my ankle.

9 WEDNESDAY

Installed on sofa with fruit, chocs, books, zapper, and a terrible itch inside my plaster cast.
Sharon offers to scratch it for me with an unfurled wire hanger — As if I would allow a wire hanger in my house!!

10 THURSDAY

still itching!

Hazelnut Surprise   Strawberry Delight

W   T   F   S | M   T   W   T   F   S   S   ~M.
2   3   4   5   6 | 7   8   9   10   11   12   13
Marcel x S

FRIDAY 11

M. returns

Marcus returns from Dubai, very tense — successful business trip. But, he had to pretend to be a Christian.

For some reason, this has made him TREMENDOUSLY RANDY........

SATURDAY 12

(MUMMY TO DINNER)

Mummy due for dinner. Marcus STILL staring at my toes with that glassy David Mellor expression. My normal caterers are busy. Sharon offers to help me out — forced to accept.

Mother's Day   SUNDAY 13

must admit — Sharon's cooking isn't bad if your idea of a Jewish meal is saveloy, mash and beans. Rather like the look of Robin, Mummy's new man — AND, as luck would have it — he's an orthopaedic surgeon!

NOTES

Countrywide caterers :— 8.00 on Saturday
071 497 1727
menu??

M	T	W	T	F	S	S		M	T	W	T	F	S	S		M	T	W	T	F	S	S
14	15	16	17	18	19	20		21	22	23	24	25	26	27		28	29	30	31			

14 MONDAY 12·00 lunch at Melanies.

Marcus and I invited to Melanie's for lunch. Find I can't sit comfortably in the Jaguar - persuade Marcus to hire a Bentley Turbo.

Melanie's face on our arrival made the fracture worthwhile!

15 TUESDAY

RONALD JENSEN CHARGED

YESTERDAY afternoon in Leeds, the well known entrepreneur, Ronald Jensen (46) was detained by officers

16 WEDNESDAY Marcus at Leeds Crown Court in the Ronald Jensen case. DETERMINED NOT TO BE HOUSEBOUND - I get an agency to send a chauffeur. George arrives. Former policeman. Impeccable manners. 15 years chauffering experience. If only I fancied him. Send him away!

17 THURSDAY   St. Patrick's Day

HUGHIE looks FANTASTIC in a chauffer's uniform. I bet when the deli sent him round with my smoked salmon, he never thought he'd end up in a uniform, in a Bentley, in Epping Forest, in the back seat WITH ME!!

FRIDAY 18

Marcus came home and SACKED Hughie - JUST because he didn't have a driver's licence. What a small minded attitude towards the problem of youth unemployment.
I BURST INTO TEARS!

SATURDAY 19

TERRIBLY DEPRESSED.

SUNDAY 20

Hobble to Marcus's wardrobe and cut the arms off his Georgio Armani dinner jacket.
Tracey pops in to ask if I want any shopping - I threaten her with pinking shears!

NOTES

Chauffeur
George Barker
arriving at
10.00am
Weds

W	T	F	S	S		M	T	W	T	F	S	S
21	22	23	24	25	26	27	28	29	30	31		

21 MONDAY

DEPRESSION OVER!! :☺-

It was just PMT. Considering what a full month I've had — physically — I ought to CELEBRATE!

22 TUESDAY

→ BENS BAR MITZVAH 2·30 — present ???

Marcus & I getting ready to go to Miriam & Tony's son's Bar Mitzvah. Marcus wants to know what happened to his D.J. — I plead ignorance — He goes next door to borrow Darryl's — VERY 1988!

23 WEDNESDAY

Sitting with the papers while Marcus is playing golf. Ring on the door, I LIMP to open it and... IT'S ROBIN — mummy's friend! He just wondered how my leg felt. I invite him to feel it & tell me!
— Wonder what FREUD would say??

24 THURSDAY ✳MARCUS IN COURT ✳

Marcus back to Leeds to give evidence. Robin comes round, AGAIN — what wonderful hands!! Of course, if he was my doctor it would be unethical as well as adulterous — BUT — WHO'S COUNTING??

© BAREFACTS DIARY 1994

FRIDAY 25

Marcus was on T.V. at lunch time!
He made <u>such</u> a mess of his evidence. he is under a cloud and <u>may</u> be charged with conspiracy to defraud.

SATURDAY 26

M. back?

Marcus arrives home <u>ABSOLUTELY</u> WRECKED.
Drank 2 glasses of advocat — A <u>LOT</u> for marcus.

Palm Sunday
Passover
British Summertime

SUNDAY 27

Marcus didn't want to get up this morning. He <u>refused</u> to come out from under the duvet, so I had to read the article in the Sunday Times out to him, conjecturing M. was the mastermind of the fraud!

NOTES

I've <u>NEVER</u> heard Marcus cry before.
(sneak out to see Robin...)

M T W T F S S | M T W T F S S | M T W T F S S
14 15 16 17 18 19 20 | 21 22 23 24 25 26 27 | 28 29 30 31

825,000
- 750,000
£75,000

28 MONDAY   PLASTER OFF - HOORAY!

Judge said M. would be in contempt
if he didn't return to court, so...
I'm alone again. Hughie phones and
invites me to an illegal rave party
instead. Danced ALL NIGHT!

29 TUESDAY

RONALD JENSEN HAS SKIPPED BAIL & fled
to Indonesia!
M. was one of his sureties to the tune
of £½ a MILLION!! WE COULD BE RUINED!
And I loved that Bentley. M. is helping
Leeds C.I.D. with their enquiries....

30 WEDNESDAY   THE HOUSE IS FOR SALE - £750,000

O.N.O. Visit M. in Leeds - he has aged 20
years. Told me I must find Ronald Jensen
& bring him back to England - feel
EXCITED & DRAMATIC! Sharon thought I was
the punchline of a joke: "My wife went
to the East Indies." "Jakarta?" "No, she
31 THURSDAY went of her own accord!" -
Interesting   STUPID WOMAN!!
few hours with the young Estate Agent -
He agreed to raise the price to £825,000.
No chance of getting a buyer at that price.
- went to Harley St. for a pre-flight check-up.
Expected armfull of injections - Got a

APRIL 1994   Bottom Full instead. Hope the plane
has well padded seats

Good Friday | HEATHROW 8·45 | *FRIDAY 1*

Half way to Bali I realised it was April Fools Day! Is this all a terrible mind up of Marcus's? It MUST Be (?) last sunday was the first night of passover - I should have been at Marcus's mother - and I was with a randy orthopaedic surgeon instead !! What a FOOL I am to fall for M's trick.

SATURDAY 2

LAND IN INDONESIA.

No idea what day it is - How many hours ahead or behind.
MUST GET BACK TO ENGLAND!!

Easter Day | *SUNDAY 3*

NO FLIGHTS - monsoon rain - apparently quite unseasonal.
Check into the Bali EMPEROR HOTEL - 5 stars & 24 HOUR MASSAGE LINE.
Maybe I'll stay a day or two...

NOTES

British Airways
Bali 626 70

M	T	W	T	F	S	S		M	T	W	T	F	S	S		M	T	W	T	F	S	S
11	12	13	14	15	16	17		18	19	20	21	22	23	24		25	26	27	28	29	30	

4 MONDAY
Easter Monday (Holiday in UK and R. of Ireland except Scotland)

<u>Easter Monday</u> — not a Bank Holiday
in Indonesia (or scotland - oddly -
according to my diary).
Decide to visit a Detective agency in
case Ronald Jensen is here.
<u>GOD — IT'S HOT!</u>

5 TUESDAY

My detective is a <u>charming</u> young man
called Pak Lok Cuk - or something like
that. He says he'll find Jensen - <u>if</u>
he's in the country, but warns me
he isn't cheap. I tell him neither am
I. — <u>I think we understand each other!</u>

6 WEDNESDAY

I have a new wardrobe made
out of silk - <u>so cheap</u> and ALL
ready in a day. Return to Hotel..
Pak Lok Cuk, he says I can call
him Cuk if I like... says he has
<del>news - but</del> is <u>VERY</u> mysterious ???

100 % PURE SILK Made in Bali

7 THURSDAY

Wake up in bed with my Indonesian
detective (?) No recollection at all of how
he got there - either I've developed
Alzheimer's overnight <u>OR</u> the local
champagne is to be avoided. But as he has
a lithe, brown, smooth body & enormous
<del>stamina</del> — <u>WHO CARES?</u>

APRIL 1994

M	T	W	T	F	S	S	M	T	W	T	F	S	S
				1	2	3	4	5	6	7	8	9	10

INDONESIA

Realize I haven't phoned Marcus! *FRIDAY 8*
DO SO. HE IS DISTRAUGHT! Thinks
I've abandoned him – As if I'd leave the
man to whom I made my marriage
vows – and who signs my visa account.
Hang up and spend rest of day in bed with...
YOU KNOW WHO!!

SATURDAY 9

One of CUK's gumshoes (technical term
for junior detectives) has found Jensen
living rough in the jungle... Suppose
I'll HAVE to go and see him.

LIVING ROUGH!!!?! Ronald Jensen has *SUNDAY 10*
a 9 bedroom, air-conditioned villa WITH
pool AND airstrip! I asked if he was
coming home to clear Marcus's
name. He just laughed and pinched
my bottom. PIG! (nice body though...)

NOTES

The Emperor Hotel
— Bali —

Notes

PACK LOCK COCK
2:00

M T W T ... W T F S S
11 12 13 14 15 ... 22 23 24 | 25 26 27 28 29 30

INDONESIA

11 MONDAY

<u>PERSUADED</u> Ronald to give me a letter exonerating Marcus.
- It took some getting out of him but .... I did what I <u>HAD</u> to do.... quite enjoyed it actually!

12 TUESDAY

Phoned M's solicitor and told him about letter.

He says 'not to worry, Marcus has had a nervous breakdown & been declared unfit to stand trial - what a <u>relief</u>!

13 WEDNESDAY

<u>SHOULD</u> go home but the weather is <u>WONDERFUL</u>! - Apparently Marcus is heavily sedated - so... what's the point??

14 THURSDAY

FOOD RIOTS IN JAKARTA...

Think I'll check out the next flight home.

APRIL 1994

M	T	W	T	F	S	S	M	T	W	T	F	S	S
				1	2	3	4	5	6	7	8	9	10

Stop over in Dubai Duty ~~Free~~ —
Feel VERY nervous in Arab country,
but manage to buy tiny video
camera — could have FUN with
it back in Blighty.

The perfect
figure for a
bikini!

→

Sun- back in
London.
POURING with
rain. Taxi home.
Big banner across
the front door...

"WELCOME HOME
YOU OLD SLAPPER!"
- Guess who's
responsible.

M	T	W	T	F	S	S		M	T	W	T	F	S	S		M	T	W	T	F	S	S
11	12	13	14	15	16	17		18	19	20	21	22	23	24		25	26	27	28	29	30	

4
BACK HOME

18 MONDAY

Visit Marcus in BUPA mental retreat (as they <u>tactfully</u> call it). He was very quiet - seemed quite normal. Only at end of visit when he confided he was really Bet Lynch on leave from 'Coronation Street' did I start to notice

19 TUESDAY something amiss.

That nice young estate agent called round. <u>AMAZINGLY</u> someone has offered £850,000 for the house. A dilemma. Should we sell?? - What if Marcus never works again?!

20 WEDNESDAY

Asked next door's advice. Tracey said she'd be sorry to see me go - Sharon said, would I leave my collection of SEX TOYS behind !? - I think she'd be secretly upset too, though.

21 THURSDAY RING IRONING SERVICE.

<u>DECIDE TO SELL</u> - buy a flat in Regent's Park, and the change should yield an income of £3000.00 per month. I <u>COULD</u> live on that, just, if I'm frugal. <u>TELL MARCUS TOMORROW</u>.

APRIL 1994

M	T	W	T	F	S	S		M	T	W	T	F	S	S
				1	2	3		4	5	6	7	8	9	10

VISIT MARCUS AT BUPA 10.00   FRIDAY 22

Marcus is no longer Bet Lynch - He's
now PC Fancy Smith of 'Z cars'.
I blame UK Gold. Told him I'm going
to see solicitors about obtaining power
of attorney. He just said: "Roger Z
Victor One"..... (??)

St George   SATURDAY 23
VIEWING 11.30

THE BUYERS, Mr & Mrs Dubrovsky, come
round to view the house. Not sure
what he does - looks VERY prosperous.
Nice, sensitive hands, too. She looks
a REAL COW! - too tanned, too much hair,
overdressed, ridiculous fingernails.

SUNDAY 24

Tracey asked me about the Dubrovskys.
"Was she a relation, we looked like
sisters!" CHEEK!! Sharon was SURE
she'd seen him on the telly.
    Maybe he's a Russian film star?

NOTES

$$\begin{array}{r} 850,000 \\ - \ 375,000 \\ \hline 475,000 \end{array}$$ per month?
interest?

@ 8·92% = approx £3000 p.m.??

25 MONDAY

HOUSE SALE OFF – Dubrovsky
not a Russian film star – he's a
Russian black marketeer with
a false passport who has just been
extradited to Moscow.

26 TUESDAY { MANICURE & PEDICURE
✱ { 2.30 PM

Marcus much better today.
Thinks he's Doctor Finlay –
which is at least a step up the
social ladder.

27 WEDNESDAY

M's solicitor phoned – The Ronald
Jensen case is falling apart through
lack of evidence. The judge is
expected to throw it out today.
Will I tell Marcus the good news?

28 THURSDAY [BUPA : 10.30]

Visit Marcus. Try to explain about
the court case. His reputation is
now restored. Marcus says he never
had any doubt. – After all, EVERYONE
knows Rumpole of the Bailey is an honest
man.

FRIDAY 29

WOKE UP VERY DEPRESSED.
Realized I hadn't had a man
for weeks! – Get my address book
out to start phoning round when
in walks Marcus – He's discharged
himself.

SATURDAY 30

start day in dreadful suspense – who
will M. think he is today??! Wonder
about hiding the 'Radio Times'. Confide
my fears to S & T who laugh at me.
Obviously Marcus had only been
pretending to be mad to avoid the trial –
I rush home & confront him. He says
he can't believe my naivety. Of course
he was pretending.
(maybe there's more
to M. than meets the eye?)

now that
is sexy!

SUNDAY – one thing
hasn't changed
re Marcus – He's
still as sexy as
a plate of tripe.
MUST GET LAID –
thouroughly & soon!!

© BAREFACTS DIARY 1994

2 MONDAY

Decide to go shopping to see what I can pick up. Wander round local supermarket with arms full of Clingfilm. GORGEOUS young branch manager called Jason asks if he can be of assistance. ~~I arrange to meet him on Wednesday~~

3 TUESDAY   BRUCE OLDFIELD SHOW 2·30PM ?

Melanie comes over to ask if I want to go to the Bruce Oldfield fashion show - She sees all the clingfilm. Strange, she doesn't ask what it's for - Perhaps she knows.... Tracey comes in and asks. I say 'what do ~~you normally use clingfilm for?~~' Tracey

4 WEDNESDAY   says "wrapping cucumbers."

MEET JASON - He asks   EXACTLY! about the bulk buying of clingfilm - what is it with clingfilm?? We take his car, an Opel Kadett, to see Top Gun 2. He's seen it 3 times, but he likes it. I suggest we go for a drive. Park the car on Hampstead Heath. It's PITCH BLACK! I ~~tell him I can now show him what the clingfilm~~

5 THURSDAY   was for - but I haven't got any cling-

(film with me - we use Bacofoil. Its not wake up   the same - DON'T try it! feeling

DREADFUL. I bet I caught something on Hampstead Heath last night.... this morning! I mean, who in their right mind would lay down on wet grass, NAKED, at the begining of May? ~~And believe me - BACOFOIL ISN'T WATERPROOF!~~

M	T	W	T	F	S	S	M	T	W	T	F	S	S
30	31						1	2	3	(4)	5	6	7	8

JASON & THE CLINGFILM!

FRIDAY 6

List
- more Lemsip
- Aspirin
- Tissues
- Ginseng
- Throat Sweets

I AM NOT WELL.

Marcus leaves me some Lemsip by the bedside.

SATURDAY 7

Feel lousy. Feel even worse when a new Crime Prevention officer calls to talk about security. He says he can give me as much time as I like. Why do men who look like this — (Gerard Depardieu) only seem to call when I'm ill?

SUNDAY 8

I ask if he could come back on Thursday ??

SUNDAY: Tracey comes in and 'does' for me. She sits and talks, as freely as she can, about her sex life with Darryl. She's never been with another man! How can she compare ??

NOTES

Jason

Tel: 623 6399

M	T	W	T	F	S	S	M	T	W	T	F	S	S	M	T	W	T	F	S	S
9	10	11	12	13	14	15	16	17	18	19	20	21	22	23	24	25	26	27	28	29

Ascension Day

Feel a little better this morning.
Suggest to M. - 'perhaps I ought to go
somewhere warm for a few days?' He
says 'Bournemouth.' I say Antigua. He
says he can't get the time off.
Why should that bother me?

10 TUESDAY The cold has gone. The sore
throat has started. still - it sounds
sexy on the phone! Another hunk
calls - to read the gas meter. Just
my luck! 2 men in 4 days I would
happily have performed the MOST
indecent acts upon, and I'm laid up...

11 WEDNESDAY BOOK SESSION AT HEALTH CLUB

Feel MUCH ...not laid! What makes
better this my illness worse is Marcus
morning - keeps phoning to see how
particularly as I am !
I booked the flight
to Antigua.

12 THURSDAY

Ask Tracey if she would come with me to
buy swimwear - although I shall go
TOPLESS - naturally. The Crime Prevention
Officer returns - His name is Douglas and I
ask him if he thinks my bedroom is
secure? We discuss this over gin & tonics.

S, T & I take taxi to Knightsbridge — FRIDAY 13
(only £52). I see a gorgeous thong in
grey leather. MUST have it. Sharon
says she wouldn't mind trying
one on. THIS I HAVE TO SEE! Tracey puts
her off it — Thank God. Buy one for each day
Also some, (8) outfits, for the evening, through the

ANTIGUA — 12.30 HEATHROW | thongs should
be more than
Fly to Antigua — M. sees me off. Tears enough
fill his eyes (petrol fumes). Sit next to
a black god called KENELM — It's
an old English name which means
BRAVE HELMET — I SHOULD BE SO LUCKY!!

Weather S.E.N.S.A.T.I.O.N.A.L. SUNDAY 15

Boy who brings my breakfast —
SENSATIONAL. Says he's never done it
before with a white lady. Keeps
calling me 'Ma'am'. Who DOES he
think I am? The Queen? Dine with
KENELM...
NOTES

* Don't forget
to book Mrs. Pearson
to 'do' for M. while
I'm away *

M	T	W	T	F	S	S		M	T	W	T	F	S	S		M	T	W	T	F	S	S
9	10	11	12	13	14	15		16	17	18	19	20	21	22		23	24	25	26	27	28	29

ANTIGUA   RETURN

16 MONDAY

'BRAVE HELMET' - what a night!
This man used to be a professional
athlete and together we did a
MARATHON! - Only it wasn't my feet which
were sore this morning.... M. phones to
see how I am. I tell him I think I'm
going down with something....

17 TUESDAY

sunbathe again. He feels sorry he isn't
ALL day with me. I THANK my lucky stars.
in the navy
strong. An American business man called
Edward says I have the 'greatest' ass in
Antigua. By 'greatest' - he means 'best.'
Sharon has the greatest in terms of
VOLUME....

18 WEDNESDAY

Edward is 'into' oil - works for MOBIL.
As I too am into oil (rubbed lightly
ALL over my body) we hit it off in
a BIG - and I do mean BIG - way!

19 THURSDAY

Edward is a group consultant and
he calls another member of this
group, DEAN, to play a little game
that involves three people, a yam
and oil - THIS IS THE LIFE!!!

MAY 1994

M	T	W	T	F	S	S		M	T	W	T	F	S	S
30	31					1		2	3	4	5	6	7	8

CONFIRM FLIGHT.

Wake up to find Edward and Dean AND JERRY (!) all in my bed. Those rum punches made me forget what the 4 of us did. But Jerry captured it all on video. BOY!! how is it possible to....? MUST try to see something of ANTIGUA today.

MUST catch some sun. Marcus is bound to ask why I am the same colour as I was in London. - Spend the day in the sun with kenelm — ME on top. I want the sun on my back. OH! KENELM! I want to marry you!!

Pentecost

RETURN TO LONDON - Fly back to London with sunburn. My back is raw. My back, my ass, as Edward called it, AND the soles of my feet. I was on "mount" kenelm for 6 hours, and the oil he rubbed all over me wasn't Ambre Solaire, but coconut oil. Apparently it TASTES better!!

M	T	W	T	F	S	S	M	T	W	T	F	S	S	M	T	W	T	F	S	S
9	10	11	12	13	14	15	16	17	18	19	20	21	22	23	24	25	26	27	28	29

KENELM!

23 MONDAY

Marcus is at home so I go next door to S&T. Tell them about Kenelm, Edward, Dean, Jerry and the room boy whose name I never asked. They think I am a SLUT! Well, Tracey does. Sharon asked to see the video!

24 TUESDAY

Meet Melanie in Selfridges - she asks about the video. I ask how SHE knows about it? - She bumped into Sharon in the french Deli. I say I'll only show her mine if she shows me her's. Bet she's never had 3 at the same time - well, not at the SAME time !!

25 WEDNESDAY

M. says with the new technology soon he'll be able to work from home FULL TIME. HE HAS TO BE JOKING. - My sex life would come to a standstill. I try & pacify him. Tonight we do it for the 2nd time in 1994 - I think of Kenelm....

26 THURSDAY

SOTHEBY'S AUCTION 10·00

071 495 3831 SUITE 6

Auction at Sotheby's - interested in 2 items of 17th century torture apparatus. I make some FURIOUS bidding, but lose out on both to a Kenyan named Joseph..... - He's GOT to be worth knowing.

MAY 1994

M	T	W	T	F	S	S		M	T	W	T	F	S	S
30	31					1		2	3	4	5	6	7	8

Buy present for Craig.

~~AUNTIE SADIE'S 7.30 pm~~

Auntie Sadie invites M & I to dinner. She's 77 and doesn't look a day over 70 - she wants Marcus to help her boyfriend's son. He's there - he's DELICIOUS - I want to help him. His name is Rodney. I bump into him in the toilet - he's coming out as I'm going in. We BOTH finish up in the bath !!...

Rodney phones to apologise for 'shtupping' me — He didn't mean to. COURSE HE MEANT TO! He wants to have an affair with me.

I don't know!

BAR MITZVAH — BRIGHTON

Trinity Sunday

To Brighton for M's nephew Craig's bar mitzvah. What an evening! D.U.L.L. I've been to brighter shiva's. However, Craig's teacher, Rabbi Sherman, is very interesting. He showed me the new shul's social club hall.... by night. How do you move in on a RABB!??

M! AGAIN!

30 MONDAY — order more flowers for ~~next week~~ Bank Holiday

Sharon comes in - wants me to buy tickets for her sponsored run...
Sharon - running??

31 TUESDAY

- TOTAL workout at health club. 2.30pm
- facial at Harrods 11.00 am.
  `nails too??

1 WEDNESDAY

GLORIOUS day for gardening. MURDO'S BACK - he's en route to Canada for a Highland Games - his plane was delayed, so he popped in "for Auld Lang Syne" to help me with my pruning...

2 THURSDAY

Nearly had a heart attack - Murdo left his sporran in the spare jacuzzi. Marcus tried to kill it with a golf club - he thought it was a RAT! Had to persuade him it was a Vivienne Westwood fashion accessory!

M	T	W	T	F	S	S	M	T	W	T	F	S	S
		1	2	3	4	5	6	7	8	9	10	11	12

⟨MARCUS AWAY⟩ Drove Marcus to Heathrow - he's off to New York to sort out the accounts of an obscure religious sect. While he was checking in... a GORGEOUS young porter in that new snazzy uniform asked if he could help with my luggage. I said I wasn't going anywhere - He said he'd see about that....

BACK to the airport for my date with DICK - (I kid you not, dear diary) - He took me into the freight elevator and asked me if I wanted to join the 100 foot club??

Invited S&T round in a moment of weakness - Sharon brought her work with her - 200lb of pickling onions to peel. Apparently her pickled onions are a big hit in cafe society & she peels them day & night to keep up with demand.

Don't forget night cream from Harrods.

DICK!!
666 1772
ext 6269

WHOLE HOUSE STINKS.

© BAREFACTS DIARY 1994

Luigi's Leathers
676 2047

BLOCKED PIPES?

SUPER-ROD

FOR COMPLETE SATISFACTION

PHONE 696969

M. still away —
HOORAY!! — Phoned SUPER-
ROD about blocked sink.
25 year old HUNK came —
tight jeans (no pants) — came
round. Asked where's the blockage?
I said 'Drains OK now, but
while you're here..... Had to
pay overtime (well worth it !!)

8 *WEDNESDAY*

WEDS — Sharon popped round to ask if
I fancied trying a new wine bar, but I
was too sore. Mother phoned. Her new
man's chumped her.
    As Pete Townsend said: "Hope I die
before I get old".

9 *THURSDAY*

FRIDAY 10

Mother called **again**. Wants to come and stay.
  Then Marcus phoned from New York – he's lonely. Decided to send Mummy to keep him company.

SATURDAY 11

Tracey anxious when I popped over. Seems Garth's been hanging out with some bikers – Asked **my** advice. I said I'd talk to them. Went 'up West' to buy a tight leather cat suit – You never know!!

SUNDAY 12

Found the bikers café. Garth fancies the girl behind the counter. I told her he had a starring role in EASTENDERS. She wa: all over him!!
– Turned my attention to ROCKY & RAZOR, 2 mustachioed Hells Angels. I wrinkled my nose wickedly & told them I thought they could both do with a bath.

NOTES

Alf's café
146 William St
(near Joes)

THEY SAID: Are you offering??
I SAID YES!.....

13 MONDAY

ACTING ALL OVER.!!

14 TUESDAY

Rocky & Razor are refusing to leave.
Then, M called to say he's coming
home!! Rushed next door — Sharon
offered to get some heavies round,
Tracey suggested a cash bribe (went
with Tracey's plan).

✳ ⟨*15 WEDNESDAY*⟩ M's BIRTHDAY✳

A.B.S.O.L.U.T.E.L.Y KNACKERED! and Marcus
is demanding his conjugal rights. I said:
"What do you think this is — your birthday?"
HE SAID YES! Embarrassment. I pretented
it was a joke, rushed to my den & gave
him the present I was keeping for my lovely,

⟨*16 THURSDA*⟩ sweet SVEN when he comes
back from SWEDEN.

Pretended I'd rediscovered God.
Told Marcus I was going to the
synagogue.
Went next door & slept for TEN hours.!.

JUNE 1994

	M	T	W	T	F	S	S	M	T	W	T	F	S	S
				1	2	3	4	5	6	7	8	9	10	11	12

Massage 11·30

* Buy Sven a welcome back
pressie?

M.'s parents ——— SATURDAY 18

My in-laws visited
TOO DULL to waste ink on.

SVEN ??

Father's Day   SVEN'S BACK!! On leave from the SUNDAY 19
Swedish Air Force — and I've given his
suede posing pouch to Marcus, who
thinks it's for keeping his golf balls
dry!
Made it up to Sven in several other
ways!

NOTES

DO NOT FORGET:
Birthday Present
for Marcus.

20 MONDAY

Woke up with 3 more grey hairs – luckily they've not on my head! Sven is at the Post House. Told Marcus I had a charity lunch. He said, "If you were having an affair, would you tell me?" I said, "Of course not." – which <u>seemed</u> to satisfy him.

21 TUESDAY

The boy from <u>SUPER-ROD</u> called back. His name's GAVIN. I didn't think to enquire before. Told me he had a new high pressure hose he wanted to demonstrate. I thought – WHY NOT??

22 WEDNESDAY

gynae? gynea

→ <u>DOCTOR LEVY 11·30 AM</u>
Went to my gynaecologist for regular check-up. He said everything seems OK – did his normal joke of saying if he wasn't my doctor, he'd HAVE to ravish me and STILL presented me with a <u>HUGE</u> bill.

23 THURSDAY

I'M PREGNANT !!!

HOW CAN THIS BE??? Dr. Levy says there's <u>NO DOUBT ABOUT IT</u>!

JUNE 1994

M	T	W	T	F	S	S	M	T	W	T	F	S	S
		1	2	3	4	5	6	7	8	9	10	11	12

FR

Actually went to the synagogue and prayed — certain I heard God laughing.

＊

Buy a present for tomorrow.
＊

THE LEV

116 HARLEY STRE
TELEPH

INVOICE NO: 086

＊ FATHER'S BIRTHDAY ＊

SUNDA

Mummy came round — always gets depressed on father's birthday. As I felt suicidal too, it wasn't much fun.

NOTES

Post House Hotel
Room no:
69

27 MONDAY

I've <u>always</u> believed in a woman's right to choose - but now I'm knocked up, I don't know if I can go through with a termination. The problem is - WHO'S THE FATHER?? <u>make a list</u>

28 TUESDAY <u>MEN I'VE HAD RECENTLY:</u>

1. Sven
2. Gavin
3. Eric
4. Peter

5. Geoff
6. That guy from the wine Bar
7. Rocky
8. Razor - only one thing for it - Seduce Marcus & persuade him its his.!!

29 WEDNESDAY

Spend day planning seductive evening. fine wine, soft music, make sure M. gets a good look at my stocking tops - the he announces the Inland Revenue are auditing their books and it's rendered him IMPOTENT!

30 THURSDAY

Buy Marcus' favourite stockings

J   M T W T F S S | M T W T F S S

1 2 3 | 4 5 6 7 8 9 10

WOW!!

- Phone call from Dr. Levy. *FRIDAY 1*
He tells me they mixed up the test
results .... I'M NOT PREGNANT!
Its a Donen Green of Chingford. I
told him I didn't want to be his
patient ANY longer. He promptly
asked for a date!!

SATURDAY 2

Just had INCREDIBLE SEX
in the back of Dr. Levy's
Range Rover —
C? I think I'm in love ♡

SUNDAY 3

NOTES

meet
Dr. Levy
1.30 pm

Independence Day, USA

Decide to celebrate by making shopping trip to New York. Booked ordinary British Airways ticket - turned up at Heathrow. Made LOUD noises about flying VIRGIN, and they bumped me up to Concorde - Always works.

Left Bloomingdale's sales staff in a state of shock. Then on to Museum of Modern Art. Stood in front of CARL ANDRE arrangement of empty toilet rolls until an interesting young man made eye contact. His name's GREGOR - He's GORGEOUS!

GREGOR IS INSANE !! I'm trapped in his loft in Alphabet City. He says - to add insult to injury - that he can't let me go because I remind him of his MOTHER!

Escaped from Gregor by offering to have sex with him as long as he called me MUMMY.
   His psyche couldn't cope and he broke down.

RETURN HOME FROM N.Y.C. 🍎 *FRIDAY 8*

Back in London - Had Marcus missed me? Apparently NOT. At dinner he said: "You've been very quiet lately, have you got a sore throat?" INSENSITIVE SWINE.

SATURDAY 9

Popped next door to see if there were any messages for me. Sharon said someone called GREGOR had left an odd message about visiting me with a MACHETE!! - She gave him my address - of course.

SUNDAY 10

Persuaded Marcus to buy a security system immediately, on account of the upsurge of crime in Greater Essex. He agreed - as long as I make all the arrangements.

NOTES

? ?

© BAREFACTS DIARY 1994

	F	S	S		M	T	W	T	F	S	S
		22	23	24		25	26	27	28	29	30	31

11 MONDAY

081-624 6242

Phoned a few
security companies —
Maybe they'll send
round some interesting
young men.....

744 6243

· alarms
· windows
· lights?

12 TUESDAY STRONG LOCK 10·00   Holiday (N. Ireland)

Strong lock consultants called - in the
shape of ALISTAIR McCORMACK. A scottish
bodybuilder who would have been
drummed out of the 'Chippendales' for being
over-muscled. Showed him round the
house. Spent rather a long time in the
master bedroom...

13 WEDNESDAY ✱ M. AWAY ✱

Marcus off to Penzance for 2 days
— back Friday

14 THURSDAY

Alistair back with his special apparatus.
He offered to wire me up for £500 —
A Bargain! Half an hour later I
was secured to the bed by several lengths
of electrical cable .... Nice — but not
what I had in mind.

JULY 1994

M	T	W	T	F	S	S	M	T	W	T	F	S	S
				1	2	3	4	5	6	7	8	9	10

FRIDAY 15

<u>LUCKILY</u> M. didn't return from Penzance last night as Alistair went to the car for something & locked himself out !! Spent the night in BONDAGE! (Thank GOD for a strong bladder). Had to use <u>nose</u> to phone Tracey to rescue me !!

SATURDAY 16

Have decided to <u>renew</u> my New Year's resolution to be faithful to Marcus — and take up some-thing worthwhile. But what??

S U N D

STRONGLOCK
THE BEST IN HOME SECURITY

ESTIMATE No: 0176
DATE: 12.7
OUR REF: 6267

ESTIMATE

TO INSTALL SECURITY SYSTEM AND REPLACE EXISTING LOCKS AND

M
11

— get some designer tags done???

__Bought a knitting machine__ — I'm going to make __colourful__ and __original__ sweaters for sale & become a famous designer — Despite the cynical comments of those 2 peasants next door.

19 TUESDAY

gold knitted vest with sequins??

Make my FIRST piece of original knitting — a small place mat. Even Kaffe Fassett started somewhere! Showed it to Marcus who said it was too small to be a skull cap.

20 WEDNESDAY

'madonna' style knitted corset??

SENT THE KNITTING MACHINE BACK. Waste of time when I can afford __any__ clothes I want. Think I'll take up something more practical. __MUST__ be lots of eligible young studs at motor mechanics class...

21 THURSDAY

Signed up for motor mechanics at the Evening Institute. NO MEN AT ALL! just women either looking a) for men or b) for other women. Don't think I'm quite ready for my first Sapphic experience.

JULY 1994	M	T	W	T	F	S	S	M	T	W	T	F	S	S
					1	2	3	4	5	6	7	8	9	10

FRIDAY 22

Alistair came back - full of apologies and aftershave. He said 'What must he do to make it up to me?' So..... I tied him to the bed - and went shopping !!

SATURDAY 23

Today I met JACQUES, a french security expert. QUELLE HUNQUE .He came round to tender for our new security system. I wanted to give it to him right away - the job - but M. insisted we see more than one expert. FAIR ENOUGH !!

SUNDAY 24

Alistair phoned with a new quotation. Shall I take him up on it..??

NOTES

Are you BORED?
Do you want a CHALLENGE?
Why not learn a new skill?
The Further Education College is offering a wide range of subjects fot those who want to have a go at something new this summer.
For more details of the many courses ....ble, ring Julia on:
081 999 8989

M T W

11 12 13

29 30 31

25 MONDAY

Saw Kim & Wing — two Korean students working their way through college by selling security systems — INCREDIBLE, lithe, muscular, hairless bodies — God! — I'm quivering just to ~~think~~ of it...

26 TUESDAY

Interviewed ROGER ex MI5 — he says — so what he doesn't know about secret places isn't worth knowing!

27 WEDNESDAY

STAYED IN BED ALL DAY, wonderfully — how can I put it — SHAGGED OUT!!

28 THURSDAY

M. asked which security company I preferred and I had to say KIM & WING — 2 Koreans in the bush are better than one in the hand.... or whatever!!

PAY MRS. PEARSON

Marcus interviewed Kim & Wing all day.

After they went he was VERY silent and thoughtful.

Marcus has decided to become a Buddhist. It seems K & W told him his obsession with home security denotes a restless soul and he needs to find inner peace through chanting and sexual abstinence — He shouldn't find the latter too hard!!!

Have to postpone security plans indefinitely until M. finds inner peace and harmony ??!!

Mrs Pearson owed £35.00 for July - check when she's away.

M	T	W	T	F	S	S	M	T	W	T	F	S	S	M	T	W	T	F	S	S
11	12	13	14	15	16	17	18	19	20	21	22	23	24	25	26	27	28	29	30	31

© BAREFACTS DIARY 1994

1 MONDAY

<u>I'M BORED !</u>

Nothing on T.V. - <u>no man</u> for <u>weeks</u> & M. deeply into his ZEN BUDDHISM. Think I'll get the house re-modelled. Told Marcus it wouldn't cost more than £100k - He said OH!

2 TUESDAY

Phoned a succession of interior designers out of the best magazines, arranged a series of visits.

Went to WAX FACTOR (the new beauty place) for strategic hair removal in anticipation.

3 WEDNESDAY 4 Designers came round today - 3 were gay, the fourth was straight <u>and</u> good looking. Unfortunately, Chris was short for Christine.

Didn't invite any of them to open their portfolios.

4 THURSDAY 10.30 - LARRY

Larry came at 10.30 and changed my life. 6'3", (29) graduate of the Slade school of fine Art, built like a bull & prepared to do the <u>whole</u> house for a mere £50,000. I managed <u>NOT</u> to say "Shall we start in the bedroom!!"

AUGUST 1994

	M	T	W	T	F	S	S	M	T	W	T	F	S	S
	1	2	3	4	5	6	7	8	9	10	11	12	13	14

FRIDAY 5

Larry has some VERY UNUSUAL ideas about decor.

Very keen on the unusual positioning of furniture and light fixtures.

Hope he likes the positions I intend to suggest.....

SATURDAY 6

Not sure BLACK is the ideal colour for the living room — BUT — Larry says an artist must be given his head......
GOOD IDEA!

SUNDAY 7

UNCLE HARRY 12.30 Went out with Marcus to visit an aged uncle of his who might leave him some money. When we returned Larry had started work — He had cleared all the furniture from the dining room & burned it!!
Not sure this is going to work out

NOTES

remember port for Uncle Harry

WORLD OF INTERIORS AUG '94

LARRY BOOTH
INTERIOR DECORATOR
Interesting Interiors for Interesting People
071 772 7777

M	T	W	T	F	S	S		M	T	W	T	F	S	S
15	16	17	18	19	20	21		22	23	24	25	26	27	28

8 MONDAY

Item in local paper about deranged former art student talking himself into people's homes & wrecking them. ~~Luckily~~ I only paid him the first £10,000

STUDENT WRECKS HOMES

A 26-YEAR-OLD art student from West London, posing as a qualified interior designer, was helping police with their enquiries today.

Larry Bernard Booth of Wickham Place, placed advertisements in magazines an...

10 WEDNESDAY Think it might be time for a holiday, as my spirits are shattered.

I know its the time of year the plebs go away — but there must be somewhere exclusive....?

11 THURSDAY

Marcus says he doesn't need a holiday because he has found inner peace & Uncle Harry has promised to leave him half a million.

(I think the old fraud is lying to get more visits). Don't want to go away alone.

AUGUST 1994

M	T	W	T	F	S	S	M	T	W	T	F	S	S
1	2	3	4	5	6	7	8	9	10	11	12	13	14

Dare I take
Sharon & Tracey??

Talk about holidays with the Cockneys. There is a difference of opinion. I favour a cultural safari through North Africa — they want to go to Disneyworld.!

Spent all day with S & T and a pile of holiday brochures. Had to persuade Sharon NOT to go topless — the world isn't ready. As usual, they're short of money — if it's going to be the Aga Khan's Sardinian resort — I'll have to subsidise.

Sardinian
Secrets (The Times)
071 222 1267

NOTES
PACKING LIST
1. JANET REGER LINGERIE
2. SUPERTAN
3. PRECAUTIONS!
4. M'S CREDIT CARD.

M	T	W	T	F	S	S	M	T	W	T	F	S	S	M	T	W	T	F	S	S
15	16	17	18	19	20	21	22	23	24	25	26	27	28	29	30	31				

15 MONDAY

Booked Sardinia through Marcus's travel Agent - told him it was for a 3 woman residential course.

16 TUESDAY

Marcus STILL sitting cross legged in the box room wearing a bed sheet! - Decide to leave him to it.

17 WEDNESDAY TO SARDINIA ⋅ö⋅

Airport a nightmare - Let the cockneys run riot in Duty Free while I found the 1st Class Lounge - Lovely, handsome attentive staff - all gay, alas. On the flight was invited to join mile high club by fat, smelly businessman. Told him

18 THURSDAY

I was a founder member & didn't go in for sex with SLUGS!

NOT A BAD HOTEL, but then it is £150 a night. S & T complaining about lack of fried breakfast facilities - Pretended I didn't know them and spent the morning poolside. Thought I spotted RUPERT EVERETT - but it can't be

FRIDAY 19

IT IS!! Rupert Everett is staying here - incognito - while learning his lines for his new film - he plays the Bad Guy in BATMAN 3!! Told him I was an English graduate and offered to read with him....

SATURDAY 20

R & I are inseperable. S & T are GREEN! Rupert is gorgeous, attentive, gallant, and I think he's attracted to me. THANK GOD I brought all my Janet Reger!

SUNDAY 21

Went for a drive in the mountains with Rupert.
   Stopped his car and made WILD, PASSIONATE LOVE in an olive grove. This is the REAL THING - I KNOW IT!!

NOTES

Don't forget:
Send postcards!!

M	T	W	T	F	S	S		M	T	W	T	F	S	S		M	T	W	T	F	S	S
15	16	17	18	19	20	21		22	23	24	25	26	27	28		29	30	31				

22 MONDAY

I'M <u>SO</u> SCARED!! Rupert and I were kidnapped by Sicilian bandits. We're being held in a stinking cattleshed. For the first 5 hours we were tied together – never thought I'd object to ~~that~~ – BUT I DID!

23 TUESDAY

<u>GOD!</u> -This is the <u>WORST</u> experience of my life – and Rupert has gone to pieces. <u>Insists</u> he isn't R.E. at all, but a lookalike called Simon who gets work on commercials Rupert is too grand to do. <u>NEVER</u> thought Rupert would be a liar (23 WEDNESDAY) <u>AND</u> a coward!

Weds: Our captors are angry. They sent a message to Sharon and Tracey saying they wanted a million dollars for us, and Sharon said 'KEEP HER!' What to do?? I'll have to make up to one of the bandits tomorrow.

25 THURSDAY

Luigi isn't too bad once you get to know him – Nothing wrong with him a bath, or shower or dentist and abstention from garlic wouldn't cure. Manage to persuade him I fancy him <u>MADLY!</u>

AUGUST 1994

M	T	W	T	F	S	S	M	T	W	T	F	S	S
1	2	3	4	5	6	7	8	9	10	11	12	13	14

FRIDAY 26

Woke up in Luigi's sweaty grasp.
Try to wipe from my memory what I
HAD to do last night. Attempt to tip-
toe from the room but he wakes & gets
amorous. SAVED by the arrival of Italian
commandoes.

SATURDAY 27

All day ALONE in bed asleep.

SUNDAY 28

Went looking for Rupert. Tracey
says he's been arrested for non-
payment of bills and impersonating
a film-star. Not a first offence
apparently.

NOTES

DAYS

卌

D	R
1	
2	0

29 MONDAY   Bank Holiday

All day in bed <u>ALONE</u>-awake.

---

30 TUESDAY

⁎ <u>BACK TO UK</u> ⁎

End of holiday. What a delightful time - though the common slags next door enjoyed themselves well enough. Seems Sharon got off with one of the ~~airline stewards~~ I was convinced

31 WEDNESDAY batted for the other side. <u>DAMN!</u>

MARCUS HAS GIVEN UP BUDDHISM !! — and joined the Labour Party (?) He has decided our obsession with material possessions <u>must</u> be faced politically. He's also <u>threatening to buy a VAUXHALL</u>!

1 THURSDAY My <u>STUPID</u> husband !!

He's only brought home a Vauxhall brochure. Why is he so interested in a CORSA? - Perhaps he thinks they throw the models in with the car. If he thinks I'm going out in a Vauxhall......

FRIDAY 2

M says he can't join the Labour Party in a Jaguar. We have a TREMENDOUS row & I go next door to S&T. Tracey is busy writing a letter to Darryl. I glance over her shoulder - no SEXY bits at all - If my man was banged up..... OH! Never mind.

SATURDAY 3

Not talking to Marcus - No man at the moment.

I'm FORCED to read a book.

SUNDAY 4

Reading 'The Importance of Being Earnest'. That's funny - he says 'I never travel without my diary. One should always have something sensational to read in the train!' I agree entirely - except I NEVER travel by train. I also shan't travel by car if Marcus keeps up this mishigas with getting a Vauxhall.

NOTES

M T W T F S S   *M T W T F S S*   *M T W T F S S*
12 13 14 15 16 17 18   *19 20 21 22 23 24 25*   *26 27 28 29 30*

5 MONDAY

Marcus has gone to the local Vauxhall dealers - which I ought to say is <u>NOT</u> in Chigwell. I think he's gone to a place called Romford (?) or some other god-forsaken backwater. If he comes home WITHOUT the Jaguar - <u>I'm LEAVING HIM.</u>

6 TUESDAY   Rosh Hashanah

Go to Chigwell Shul - see Melanie Fishman. She tells me about her new lovers - 19 year old identical twins. They feel the same things at the same time! Rabbi Shatner tells us to be quiet - 'God can hear everything we're talking about.' No wonder he's got a long white beard !!

7 WEDNESDAY

Go into S & T's - Tracey's at a prison visit. I spend an <u>HOUR</u> trying to explain to Sharon why buying a Vauxhall is acceptable grounds for divorce - but she can't <u>begin</u> to understand (??)

8 THURSDAY M. <u>STILL</u> has the Jaguar - I am <u>STILL</u> in Bryan Close. I ask Sharon if she would take a day off and come to Romford tomorrow - I guess she would know where it is <u>and</u> speak in Romford's native tongue. She says - 'Blimey, <u>whassgoindaaninRomford</u> !!! Whatever <u>THAT</u> means ??!'

We go to the Vauxhall dealership — *FRIDAY 9*
very nice salesman — GARY. Sharon
fancies him, ('I could give that one !!') —
but I can see he's hot for me. We test
drive a CORSA — I don't like it at all. It
doesn't even have leather seats! Gary
then takes me for a spin in a FRONTERA....

The Levitts — Lunch 12.30) The suspension *SATURDAY 10*
) is INFINITELY better...

IMPORTANT clients of
M's — I get in a firm of caterers 'Red Herrings'.
Waldo — the cook — tells me they NEARLY
named a salad after him. I am about
to ask if he likes being tossed when M.
comes in for the corkscrew. Waldo says

VISIT M'S MOTHER) he will teach me ALL *SUNDAY 11*
) about slow simmering
She keeps asking) on an Aga !!...
me why we have never had children?
I tell her Marcus would rather have
a Vauxhall !!

NOTES

Waldo
0237 669491   Get caterers
                  for Saturday
              — Try 'Red Herrings??'

© BAREFACTS DIARY 1994

12 MONDAY I call Waldo and ask when he can show me how to simmer slowly until I come to the boil? He says he's doing a dinner party for a book publisher this Saturday, would I come along?? I would have to pretend to be a waitress — COUNT ME IN!!

13 TUESDAY M. receives membership forms for the Labour party — I think he's FLIPPED! This afternoon I start writing another chapter of my novel.
If I'm going to the house of a publisher, I might be able to slip something into his lap....

14 WEDNESDAY GARY telephones and asks if I would like to try a SENATOR. I ask which Senator he has in mind?? (Edward Kennedy always appealed to me). He means their 'top of the range' model. I say when can we test drive it? He says he could bring it over to me — I suggest 3.30 on Friday.

15 THURSDAY DINNER AT AUNTIE LILY'S — Yom Kippur
TODAY IS THE DAY OF ATONEMENT — I atone all night!! All of which I tell Melanie Fishman about. She gives out little shrieks of pleasure. Rabbi Shatner tells us to be quiet. — Tonight we go to Marcus's Auntie Lily to break our fast. I haven't let ANYTHING pass my lips all day.

COSMO 626 9472

3.30 GARY & THE SENATOR!

What a LET DOWN! Gary brought the Senator, not bad for under £30,000. I ask if the name and hub caps can be removed. After the test drive, I ask if he would like another one... I show him what orthopaedic suspension can feel like, but as soon as I get down to the lilac silk Janet Reger, it's all too much for him!!

DINNER PARTY WITH WALDO

Marcus asks if I would mind the Chigwell Labour Party meeting at the house - I tell him I'm going to a party so he can do what he likes as long as he uses the rubbish crockery - it seems a shame to waste Villeroy & Bosch on socialists. How many people is M expecting? '3, including himself' - I'm surprised Chigwell can run to 3 Labour Party members!!

— * —

* SUNDAY - WHAT A NIGHT!! Maybe the best of the year! Waldo & I simmer slowly on the Aga... he has a very nasty burn. I ask the publisher if he would read my novel. He says - 'Why don't I bring it to his office & read it to him?? This man has STYLE!

M	T	W	T	F	S	S		M	T	W
12	13	14	15	16	(17)	18		19	20	21

HOT STUFF!

19 MONDAY

Waldo in hospital – Second
degree burns apparently.

20 TUESDAY M. to Vienna on business – Sukkot Begins
Back Sat. Tracey asks if I would help
arrange a surprise party for Sharon.
I say I know a VERY GOOD caterer...
when is S's birthday? September 30th –
she's a virgo (some hopes!) Why does T
want to plan it now? 'Because she has
to save up' – save up?? – the working
21 WEDNESDAY classes have some very strange
habits. I agree to help.

Off to see COSMO ORBEN –
the publisher.

22 THURSDAY Good thing Marcus is away
on business !! – I didn't get home
until 7 this morning.
Cosmo publishes a book on the Marquis
de Sade and we act out the first
three chapters – FIVE to go .....!

M	T	W	T	F	S	S	M	T	W	T	F	S	S
			1	2	3	4	5	6	7	8	9	10	11

© BAREFACTS DIARY 1994

FRIDAY 23

I telephone a 'certain' video club and ask if they have a movie entitled 'POPE INNOCENT XV' – strongly recommended by Cosmo. It'll come on a pizza motorcycle (Chigwell's answer to a brown paper bag) tomorrow.

SATURDAY 24

M. returns Austria.

Watch the video about this Pope with very strong, chunky thighs and three housewives with broken dishwashers! Oh! and there's a LOT more. Marcus comes home from Vienna – I suggest we go STRAIGHT to bed! He thinks this is a good idea as he has had a rotten journey from Austria. I want bizarre sex, M. wants to tell me he's been made Deputy Chairman of the Chigwell LABOUR party!!

certain VIDEO CLUB

16 High Street Chigwell 98945

☆ AMAZING NEW TITLES
☆ EXCELLENT VALUE
☆ OPEN ALL DAY, EVERY DAY
☆ MAKE SURE YOU'RE certain...

No: 5724

26 MONDAY

Melanie comes over to ask if I would be interested in SWAPPING Cosmo for identical twins??

27 TUESDAY Tracey pops in. She's anxious about Sharon's surprise party. I tell her I will ask Cosmo what he thinks would be a good idea – T. thought a male strippergram might be a good laugh... Do I know anyone? HONESTLY??

28 WEDNESDAY Tracey is FRANTIC about Sharon's party. I tell her I've been given the name of a very UNUSUAL cateringfirm. I call and speak to a man called INNES. He takes my address & the time I shall be in.... alone – tomorrow.

(10.30 Innes)

29 THURSDAY Innes comes around. His firm, THE ZULU WARRIORS, specialize in African cuisine. Where they differ from other outfits like Jewish catering firms is all the waiters are men, NAKED MEN. Choose 4. Innes tells me a selection of dips will take on a whole new meaning at this party!!

OCTOBER 1994

M	T	W	T	F	S	S	M	T	W	T	F	S	S
31					1	2	3	4	5	6	7	8	9

SHARON'S BIRTHDAY

FRIDAY 30

I go in at about 9 & give her a 2 month subscription to <u>weight watchers</u> which M. & I thought was rather apt. I also give her a <u>very</u> rude card which says.... 'Big, Black & Beautiful'- Sharon says she wouldn't mind waking up next to him!! -Isn't she in for a SURPRISE.... !!

SATURDAY 1

Last night T. took S. to the wine bar, S didn't want to go, T. insisted, They rowed, walked into Dakentrace and there were 20 friends (most of them common oiks from N. London who one shouldn't really encourage to come to chigwell), and 4 waiters.... naked, except for bowler hats. The night went with a BANG!..... for me & carlton!

SUNDAY 2

wear some <u>seriously</u> sexy underwear and book a taxi to cosmo's house. Tonight we are - apparently - reading excerpts from 'In Praise of Panty Hose' by Sabina Sedgewick. There will be 9 of us - 7 MEN & 2 WOMEN!!

NOTES

ORDER SOME V. SPICY DIPS FROM THE CATERERS

© BAREFACTS DIARY 1994

3 MONDAY Just in case this diary ever falls into the wrong hands — it's better I don't record what I actually <u>did</u> last night... Met 'Vernon', a prominent Tory MP, at the reading. He invited me to the House of Commons for lunch.

4 TUESDAY I won't say who he is, but I'd know him naked!!!

M. gets Vauxhall Corsa. They do a tremendous range of colours, I have to say. M. chooses grey - typical of the man. Cosmo would have gone for a shocking pink. We are <u>keeping</u>

5 WEDNESDAY the Jaguar. M says <u>I</u> can drive it.

M. is invited as a delegate to the Labour Party Conference. Who is he a delegate of?? The National Union of Jewish Chartered Accountants and ulcer sufferers??

6 THURSDAY Melanie comes over. Tell her — in <u>STRICTEST</u> confidence, all about the literary circle, Sabina Sedgewick and her novel. Melanie is GREEN with envy - I have her eating out of my hand.

M	T	W	T	F	S	S		M	T	W	T	F	S	S
31					1	②		3	4	5	6	7	8	9

M.P. !!

© BAREFACTS DIARY 1994

FRIDAY 7

Sharon comes in and says Cosmo is on the phone. Well - I couldn't give him my home number, could I ??

SATURDAY 8

Cosmo is acting as intermediary for 'Vernon' and invites me to go to Prime Minister's Question Time on 13th. 'Vernon' thinks I could go down very well on/in Conservative circles!!

SUNDAY 9

Cosmo asks if I would like to join 'CLITS'- Charleston Literary and Intellectual Society - Apparently Charleston was where the Bloomsbury Set used to hang out. I say 'count me in'... but Cosmo says I have to be interviewed for membership. Could I attend his home ?? - Can a fish swim ??

NOTES

10 MONDAY <u>CLITS</u> Tell M. I'm going to the Jewish Women's Guild. He asks if I'm happily married? I tell him I can't talk now, I'll be late for my meeting. He wants to talk about our marriage, I can go to the JWG any time — NOT <u>THIS</u> women's Guild I can't! I leave him & drive to Holland Park.

11 TUESDAY —<u>WHAT A NIGHT</u>!!

M. asks why the JWG at a local shul should go on until 2.30am? — I tell him he shouldn't bother with trivialities. 'I love you', I tell him. He gets all maudlin and says how <u>lucky</u> he is to have me. <u>I tell him not now</u> — it's been a long, hard night!!

12 WEDNESDAY

I've been invited to the Conservative Party Conference in Brighton!!! I'm booked into the GRAND!

13 THURSDAY <u>PM'S QT</u> — Drive to Westminster. 'Vernon' takes me to the Strangers Bar. I am introduced to people who are better left unnamed. Sit through PM's Question Time and <u>all</u> through it I can see a particular MP smiling up at me — HE'S GOT TO BE JOKING !!!

OCTOBER 1994

M	T	W	T	F	S	S		M	T	W	T	F	S	S
31					1	2		3	4	5	6	7	8	9

FRIDAY 14

M. is worried - last night he split the Chigwell Labour Party and a prominent member resigned - Then there were 2.... And <u>still</u> Marcus can't become Chairman!!

SATURDAY 15

M. drinks too much & starts preaching to me why the Tories are bringing this country to it's knees. I say 'I hope they bring me to my knees in Brighton...' but M. is too sozzled to hear what I said.

SUNDAY 16

DINNER AT MELANIE'S. Fishman's for dinner - Melanie's husband, Charles, & Marcus are thinking of going into business together. Charles asks M. what he can put up?
I am about to blurt out the answer but why should I ruin M's chances <u>and</u> embarrass him at the same time ??

NOTES

0273 30512
The Grand Hotel
Brighton
Suite 476
19.10. → ?

© BAREFACTS DIARY 1994

M	T	W	T	F	S	S		M	T	W	T	F	S	S		M	T	W	T	F	S	S
10	11	12	13	14	15	16		17	18	19	20	21	22	23		24	25	26	27	28	29	30

Pick up video for Melanie.

17 MONDAY

Tory party conference begins today. I am going down on Wednesday until friday. Cosmo is driving me. He has a FERRARI. I've asked him to collect me from ~~Melanie~~ Fishman's — just to see her face!!

18 TUESDAY

Melanie asks when she can meet Cosmo? I lend her the video 'Pope Innocent XV' which I copied from VHS to Betamax — ALL Jews have Betamax!

1994
ERVATIVE
IFERENCE
reen
1

WEDNESDAY

TO BRIGHTON ..... (Melanie's 10.00)

OFF TO THE CONFERENCE! My suite is next door to Cecil Parkinson .... IS THIS SAFE??

THURSDAY Attend debates in the Conference Hall, but this Tory Party is too liberal for me. Of course one <u>has</u> to vote for them, ~~there is no other party~~! EVENING: I'm discreetly ushered into a private party. Have a <u>very</u> interesting conversation with Kenneth Clarke, but conversation ~~is where it stops~~. I couldn't fancy him BAKED!!

FRIDAY 21

HEAVY night with some big knobs. In The Party, rather hungover. Bump into Lady Thatcher in the Ladies – we have a chat about being married to men who pale into insignificance when we're around. This evening is the Conservative Party Ball – and I'm going with Cosmo – decoy for 'Vernon' – SO EXCITING

SATURDAY 22

SAT: – Phone M. to tell him I'll be late. Don't mention the Conference as M. is a dyed-in-the-wool Socialist, STUPID MAN! The Ball was wonderful although I couldn't cast my spell over Michael Portillo (DAMN!) 'Vernon' took me to an alternative Ball afterwards & for discretion's sake I can only say that '<u>Ball</u>' was the operative word.

British Summer Time ends

SUNDAY 23

SUNDAY: Visit Charleston – Delightful. Virginia Woolf & her sister came here under the pretence of writing & painting, but really they used to have <u>WILD</u> parties. 'Vernon' Cosmo, 1 or 2 other Tories, and little old me re-enacted a typical weekend – 3 line whip takes on a whole new meaning!!

NOTES

M	T	W	T	F	S	S		M	T	W	T	F	S	S		M	T	W	T	F	S	S
10	11	12	13	14	15	16		17	18	19	20	21	22	23		24	25	26	27	28	29	30

BRIGHTON

24 MONDAY | massage 3.30pm | United Nations Day

Arrived home <u>LATE</u>
last night.

25 TUESDAY

Telephone rings... It's Waldo-the chef. He's had to have some skin removed from his bicep & grafted onto his right buttock. The Aga burn was really quite serious!!

26 WEDNESDAY   <u>EMPIRE 7.30 PM</u>

M. invited to the ROYAL CHARITY PREMIER of a new film. It's at the Empire, Leicester square. When I say 'Royal', it isn't <u>really</u> Royal: it's <u>only</u> Prince Edward!

27 THURSDAY

*MY BIRTHDAY * – 36 again!
Spend the day accordingly:
    Champagne, caviar and
        <u>Cosmo</u>!

J. 081 623 6974 (ex directory)

FRIDAY 28

CLITS 8PM A Junior Minister asks if he can drive my car home - WHY NOT ?? We are stopped, he's breathalysed - the crystals turn fluor-escent !! Thankfully I'm Jewish & don't drink anything stronger than cherry brandy !!

SATURDAY 29

The M.P. who must remain nameless, is charged with DRUNKEN DRIVING. I phone him - He says the story mustn't get out. Oh, a political scandal ! - NEVER been involved in one of those before. That's one in the eye for Melanie Fishman !!

SUNDAY 30

I buy ALL the papers and check the front pages. The Mirror have it: "Minister & Mystery Lady(!) in Drink Drive Adventure". How did they get the story ??

...rauey (49),
...dispute ...d will not
...re unable to commu...
Mr. Bradley has promised th... will try to have everything in the

MINISTER AND MYSTERY LADY IN DRINK DRIVE

31 MONDAY Receive an anonymous call to go to a West Ham public house — it's 'vitally important.' Sounds intriguing! I find the pub and the anonymous caller finds me. He says he's here on the Minister's behalf. I have to stand up in court & say I was driving or the Minister's career could be over.....

1 TUESDAY This is SO thrilling — who can I tell? Tracey is the only person who would keep it to herself. I find her under the sink trying to repair a leak — How unladylike. I ask if I could have a word. She asks me if I would like her plunger up some part of my anatomy I couldn't identify.!

2 WEDNESDAY M. & I to Leicester Square for film Premier

The Slaughtered Lamb (!!)
6, Nile street
2.30pm

3 THURSDAY

The film was DREADFUL — the party was FANTASTIC. Prince Edward's detective showed a lot of interest. Perhaps he can help me out of my dilemma?? Stupid Marcus only tries to 'chat up' some bimbo. Who does he think he is? the director asked if I'd ever thought of acting?? I take his number......

FRIDAY 4

Should I call Brad - the director?? Was he serious?? I find him strangely attractive. His girlfriend was <u>VERY</u> wary of me - she knows a challenge when she sees it.

SATURDAY 5

The anonymous caller calls again - I tell him I <u>can't</u> own up to driving the Minister. He tells me I'll be sorry....

SUNDAY 6

SLEEPLESS NIGHT.... I <u>must</u> tell Marcus. I suggest dinner this evening - M. <u>Knows</u> there's something wrong.

NOTES

M T W T F S S   M T W T F S S   M T W T F S S
14 15 16 17 18 19 20   21 22 23 24 25 26 27   28 29 30

7 MONDAY I tell M. I've joined a respectable Literary Circle (he was pleased). I tell him I was being driven home by a member, a male member (he was wary). I tell him the male member is an MP (he was curious). I tell him the MP is a Tory (he was angry). Then I tell him the MP was over the limit and now the Press want to

8 TUESDAY know who he was driving home - Then the bill arrived - (he was APOPLECTIC!). Two papers run with the story. The Minister's wife has left him - He will probably have to resign - OH MY GOD!!

9 WEDNESDAY | M. TO MILAN | M. dashes into the bedroom!! - There are photographers ALL over our front lawn!! M. panics! Fat lot of good he is! S & T come in. Sharon says the photographers are 'lowering the tone of the area!' THAT'S RICH - coming from her.

10 THURSDAY Photographers EVERYWHERE! Sharon suggests she be a decoy, so I can sneak out and get to Wax Factor. I am grossly insulted that Sharon thinks anyone would mistake her for me... but, it works! I come out of the 'Tradesmans entrance' for the 1st time since I've lived in Chigwell & catch a bus!! (for the

I lie low and keep
    Shtum.

(I think that's the word ??).

The DAILY MAIL call. They know
I'm the 'other' woman in the
scandal. Who tipped them off?
They offer me £25,000 to 'spill
the beans'. What a vulgar
    vocabulary.

Rememberance Sunday

— Pop in on S & T for advice — they
both say I should 'kiss and
tell!' But NOTHING happened between
me and the Minister! Sharon says
I'm making it up!

£25,000 ??

Shall I ???

14 MONDAY M. BACK — I tell him about the cash offer. He says it isn't worth it: 'After tax you would only be left with £17,000; then there are the expenses: travel, new clothes for photographs....' I'll phone the Mail tomorrow.

15 TUESDAY

Tory Party Central Office make me a counter offer. I tell them <u>nothing</u> happened but they insist they know the Minister's reputation and have wanted to get rid of him for some time, they just need proof!

16 WEDNESDAY

Murdo has landed a job as a gardener in FRANCE. He needs references and has come over to ask if I would give him one. I tell him I'd love to but I can't remember just how good he was — It was a <u>long</u> time ago......

17 THURSDAY

I give Murdo a <u>3</u> page reference.

M. asks why, if nothing went on **FRIDAY 18**
between me and the Minister, should
the Mail have offered me £25,000 and
Tory Party Central Office want to bribe me?
I look him in the eye and ask the all-
important question: 'Do you think I would
EVER be unfaithful to you, darling?' M. says
'of course not'

SATURDAY 19

Lunch with the Tories
tomorrow. M says I should ask them to
double the Mail offer. After all, he said,
they can afford it! (Is this the end of
his silly Socialist flirtation?? I HOPE
so.)

LUNCH 1.00 — WHAT a meeting! I **SUNDAY 20**
have never been so scared in my life.'
I told them I wanted £50,000 — they told
me what I could do. They said they have
photographs in their possession..... The
gentlemen, who never once told
me his name, said 'I
think we understand
each other...'   'E S

maybe I
should keep →
a low profile.

M	T	W	T	F	S	S		M	T
14	15	16	17	18	19	20		21	22

21 MONDAY

VERY FRUSTRATED

In move than one sense.

---

22 TUESDAY 'VERNON' doesn't answer my calls. Cosmo is in New York .... permanently, and when I ask M if he'd like a jacuzzi he says all that swirling water makes his appendix rumble! WHAT do I have to do to get my husband in the mood ???

---

23 WEDNESDAY JD&S ? Pop in on S&T. I ask if they'd like to go to a Jewish divorced and separated evening in Barkingside. Tracey says she isn't divorced - I point out she's separated.

---

24 THURSDAY WHAT A BUNCH OF LOSERS!! A dentist called Alan picks me up. A shoe salesman called Benny tries to pick up Tracey, until she tells him she's not Jewish; and a taxi driver called Martin tries to pick up Sharon - and gets a hernia!!

FRIDAY 25

Walking past an Estate Agents I see Luke inside. Do I go in? Can one recapture the past?? I invite him out for a drink 'for old time's sake! I suggest my place. He thinks we should go somewhere safer. I suggest his place.

SATURDAY 26

ALAN the dentist phones me ... AT HOME!! How did he get my number? Sharon gave it to him. He asks if I would like to go out next Sunday?? Martin has invited Sharon & perhaps we could make it a foursome - a foursome with Sharon?? EUGH!!

SUNDAY 27

| 7.00 |
| LUKE |

LUKE- the man who made my body work like no other before OR since, except Murdo .... or Cosmo .... Waldo took some beating. And what about the gorgeous Kenelm? No, all right, there have been others as good as Luke, but Luke was special...

NOTES

N.Y.C.

Directory Enquiries New York — 6978124

The lovely LUKE

28 MONDAY LUKE IS FREE! - His engagement to the SLUT, Carmen, is over. I suggest we try again, but he says only if I leave Marcus. Luke says he earns enough to keep us both. Does the boy know how much I cost??

29 TUESDAY Ask S & T for advice. T. says marriage is forever and I shouldn't be strumping other men. S. says I should give Marcus the heave-ho, what have I got to lose? I explain that there's the house; the Jaguar; the allowance; the 10 holidays a year; the

30 WEDNESDAY charge accounts... St Andrew

'Phone Marcus and ask if we can meet tomorrow for lunch? I want to discuss the future. He suggests meeting by Marble Arch, buying some sandwiches & sitting in Hyde Park. I suggest Le Caprice.

1 THURSDAY LE CAPRICE 1.00 PM ~ I see Nigel Havers. We smile. We don't know each other, but that could be arranged... M. arrives. I ask where our marriage is going? He doesn't understand. Just as I'm explaining, his portable cellnet goes and he has to leave.

FRIDAY 2

M. & I talk. He loves me, couldn't live without me.... 'Why don't you ever make _mad_, _passionate love to me_,' I ask. He asks what I mean. I'm married to a KLUTZ!! 'You couldn't be unfaithful to me, could you, Dolly?' He says. I say OF COURSE NOT(!!), but a woman has needs...

SATURDAY 3

Luke phones. He says if I _don't_ leave Marcus by Tuesday, he's giving up his job and going to New York. I decide to leave Marcus — But how can I tell him??

SUNDAY 4

The atmosphere between M. and myself is strained. M's cousin Sidney & Kitty come to Lunch. I cook - salmon, asparagus, Beluga caviar, the normal. I drink too much and tell Kitty I'm leaving M. She says she and Sidney expected it years ago!!

NOTES

WAYS TO TELL MARCUS:

1. Tell Sharon.
2. Tell his mother.
3. With flowers??

© BAREFACTS DIARY 1994

DECEMBER 1994

5 MONDAY ⟨HAIRCUT 10.00⟩ HOW can I give up this lifestyle?? Perhaps I'm not a one man woman..... I discuss my dilemma with Deke, my hairdresser. He says if I run off with Luke, guys like Duncan, his DISHY new junior, would be out of bounds... This DOES it. No one man can be worth

6 TUESDAY the many I would be tossing away.

↳I tell LUKE I can't run away with him. I am in TEARS! Then Duncan comes to wax my legs. I tell him to be gentle. He's 19 and when he touches my hair, let alone my legs.... PHEW!!

7 WEDNESDAY Yesterday Tracey came to borrow my lawnmower – and.... she REALLY fancies Duncan. Wonders never cease?!! I tell Duncan not to hold his breath, she is absolutely faithful – AND her husband is a dangerous criminal. We resume the leg waxing – Then my bikini line. Then..... 19 year olds have

8 THURSDAY SUCH stamina.

Take Mummy to lunch. We see Michael Caine and she asks for his autograph. I could have DIED!! HOW EMBARRASSING!!!

Then Mummy tells me Sidney has told M. I'm leaving him!! OH NO!

FRIDAY 9

SAVAGE row with M. He asks if there's someone else — I tell him there is no ONE else. In bed M. tries to be passionate, but I fall asleep. M says 'Why can't it always be like this?' LIKE WHAT?? M. books us on the Orient Express to Venice. This is the most

SATURDAY 10

romantic thing he has done whilst I've kept awake!!

→ VENICE

Sat - 10 minutes out of Dover and M. is sick. What a klutz!! We board the train in Boulogne and he takes to his bottom bunk — (afraid of heights). Dinner with an Italian called Flavia (30 & travelling alone). My lucky weekend or what?!?

SUNDAY 11

6.00am - wake up in the top bunk with Flavia!! (I am not afraid of heights). Back to my cabin to find Marcus so white he clashes with the sheets. The old hypochondriac. MILAN STATION - Flavia asks if I would run off with him. We run off back to his cabin. MAMMA MIA!!!

NOTES

The Orient Express
BOARDING CARD
LONDON
VENICE
Cabin No. 6
Carriage No. 4
Date: 10.12.94
Single

M T W T   F S S | M T W T F S S
12 13 14 15   17 18 | 19 20 21 22 23 24 25 | 26 27 28 29 30 31

12 MONDAY <u>VENICE</u> - M. takes a turn for the worse. Flavia and I take a gondola and steal <u>more</u> than a kiss under the Rialto (those hands... that tongue!). He says 'why don't we spend our last night in the Cipriani?' Isn't this where Heseltine had his heart attack??

13 TUESDAY <u>FLY BACK TO LONDON</u>. M. doesn't stop apologising for ruining my weekend!! Sharon pops in. Tracey's birthday is next Tuesday and would I keep the evening free to go to T's favourite pub in Hoxton? Can't wait — where's Hoxton??

14 WEDNESDAY

Melanie has won 2 days for 2 at a Health farm in a Jewish charity raffle. <u>COUNT ME IN</u>! She's green about Flavia - she's never had an Italian. I ask M. if he minds me going with Melanie? He says of course not, I deserve a break after he ruined my time on the Orient Express. <u>BLESS HIM</u>!

15 THURSDAY Sharon asks where I'm going with Melanie and can she come with! Mind you, she needs a Health farm more than me do. We arrive and immediately set our sights on Indian doctors, Saeed and Vishram. They ask if we would like mixed doubles this afternoon — Tennis??

The boys think we are great FRIDAY 16
fun — which we are. We have a sauna
together and a roll in the snow. Spend
the evening on the squash court with
Vishram. All that banging against the
walls gives me an appetite — I really
fancy an Indian ...

SATURDAY 17

Ask Vishram what he's doing tomorrow night —
He's going to the Temple: — it's the Martyrdom
of Guru Tegh Bahadur. Of course, should
have known! No sign of Melanie — her car's
still in the car park, so I ask reception for the
keys and drive home. I like her Aston Martin.
It would make a wonderful Christmas
present. SUNDAY 18

Melanie comes to collect her car. I ask about
last night, she just smiles. I know
what that means!!
We've both lost weight, but then we've
taken PLENTY of exercise. I should send
Tracey to the Health farm as a birthday
present.
NOTES

THINGS TO PACK:

- Tennis racquet
- All in one black exercise catsuit.
- Lycra g-string (leopard print one
- Trainers   & gold one)

© BAREFACTS DIARY 1994

19 MONDAY BOOK T.'s birthday present. Go to Harrods - Xmas shopping: spend £4000. Buy an 18-carat-gold Aston Martin key ring. See if Marcus takes the hint. For Sharon a box of chocolates and Yardley's perfume. For Tracey a British Rail season ticket to the prison of her choice.

20 TUESDAY *TRACEY'S BIRTHDAY* - she's in a foul mood. Darryl's in solitary confinement for 3 days. What can you expect with this class of person? Lunch with Melanie: ask what happened between her and Saeed?.... It'll make a marvellous new chapter for my book!

21 WEDNESDAY M's company Christmas Party

I HATE these affairs. The lower orders mix with directors like old friends. I dance with Elvis from the photocopying room. Something comes between us.... It isn't a member of staff, but it could be the staff of a member of staff!!

22 THURSDAY

Elvis asked if I was interested in the new colour copier. The next thing I know we're locked in the photocopying room with copies of my bare bottom spurting out of the machine - It was a race to see who finished last - Elvis or the copier!!

"DING DONG!"

FRIDAY 22

'Last minute' Christmas shop. Ring Fortnums and ask how large is their <u>largest</u> Christmas Hamper? They do a Christmas and New Year Survival Hamper for only £875.00 – plus free delivery. I place my order.

SATURDAY 24

<u>PARTY</u> – 8pm – <u>ANOTHER</u> office party! Elvis takes me up to the roof. It's snowing and all I've got on is my ivory mink. I ask to go inside but some joker has locked the doors – we can't even call the police .... well, we can, but they won't hear us 19 floors up.

SUNDAY 25

(Christmas Day) — HAPPY CHRISTMAS!!

'Ding, Dong merrily on high....' Finally let out by security man – home at 3.30am. Tell M. I was doing <u>intensive</u> work for 'Save The Children'. 'You're <u>such</u> a big-hearted person,' he says. We go to bed and he asks why I've got 'Merry Xmas' written in lipstick on my bum ?? – I'll <u>MURDER</u> that Elvis...

NOTES

↯
Don't forget
↳ ring mummy on christmas Day //

© BAREFACTS DIARY 1994

Bi 071 697 2424

M. **not** talking to me **and** he hasn't
given me an Aston Martin - Schnorrer!!
He hasn't given me ANY present. At least
S & T buy me a year's subscription to a male
equivalent of Penthouse - bedtime reading,
they say. I don't read at bedtime — I perform
at bedtime.

M. apologises
and gives me my present - 'Diana Her Story'.
Is he trying to tell me something? Meet
THOMAS, a dermatologist, at the Levy's party.
I see Marcus trying to flirt with the hostess so
Thomas and I go to one of the 6 loos, lock the
door and I show him a rash I keep getting...

A quiet day in bed reading my magazine.
Where do they find these men? Why can't I
find them? Sharon says they aren't really
built like this, they've been touched up. 'By
whom,' I ask? - That's a job I wouldn't mind
getting my hands dirty for.

It's been a quiet year really but
I've had some fun. If only I could tell
Marcus. If only I was brave enough to be a
single woman again. NO! It's more fun being
married, everything is heightened at the
thought of getting found out. The problem is....
M. is NEVER likely to find out.

FRIDAY 30

MELANIE'S 8pm

Is Thomas to be my
last man of '94? This
evening Marcus and I
are invited to Melanie
Fishman's New Year's Eve
Party...

✷ 1995 ✷

Sat 1st Jan

At midnight we sing
'Auld Lang Syne' and
I stand in Melanie's
new kitchen and
make my New Year's
resolutions:

- I won't spend more
  than £4000 on any
  single garment;
- I am going to attempt
  to get Tracey laid this
  year
finally
- I mustn't be unfaithful to Marcus He's a
  good man really and I'm very lucky to
  have him as a husband.

SUNDAY 1

me at Melanie's
party - Hello
1995!

NOTES

...And then I see Melanie's brother-in-
law, Braham. Now that would be a good
way to start 1995. He gives me his
telephone number... Must buy a new filofax.

M	T	W	T	F	S	S	M	T	W	T	F	S	S	M	T	W	T	F	S	S
9	10	11	12	13	14	15	16	17	18	19	20	21	22	23	24	25	26	27	28	29

2 *MONDAY* **✳ POST CHRISTMAS SESSION AT GYM ✳**

3 *TUESDAY*

4 *WEDNESDAY*

5 *THURSDAY* **MARCUS'S MOTHER FOR DINNER 6.30**

JANUARY 1995

M	T	W	T	F	S	S	M	T	W	T	F	S	S
						1	2	3	4	5	6	7	8

NAME	CODE	NUMBER
PEDRO (SPANISH WAITER, TAPAS BAR - ENORMOUS BOTTLE OPENER)	071	623 9712
JAKE (Aerobics Instructor)	071	997 6996
BILL - landscape gardener, (gorgeous dirty fingernails)		339 2496
HUGO - petrol pump attendant who inflated my tyres (WHAT A BLOW JOB!)	071	772 6938
PIERS - french chef at the San Michelle - saucy boy!	071	889 8832
HORACE - Mummy's bowel specialist	071	779 3962
RABBI GRUNWALD (Reformed, sexy, must be temptable ?!?)	071	623 9472
ROBERT REDFORD (the one who works at WH Smiths but he has a nice smile anyway)	071	634 4986
* ALONZO - Melanie Fishman's hairdresser - MUST have him eventually *	071	997 2631
MARCUS - CAR PHONE	0836	225255
ANNE SUMMERS 24 HOUR ORDER LINE		0973 621111

TELEPHONE NUMBERS

NAME	CODE	NUMBER
DEKE – my hairdresser – lovely but camp as a row of pink tents – MUST get him off with Melanie		(911 6263)
George McTaggart – hypnotherapist ☺ (sexy if aloof)	0297	9121166
→ MUMMY	071	998 9916
MRS PEARSON, my dear old cleaner.... she means well		071 992 8413
TROY, mobile masseur (lovely supple fingers)		767 6677
SINGLES – 24 hour chat line	0898	987 654
∗ SVEN in Sweden c/o Wing Command		400 835
ODDS & SODS SERVICES very handy around the house!	071	852 9210
VITS-R-US – Vitamins Delivery Line —	081	860 0695
Topsy Turvy Wine Bar	081	240 1467
House of Commons – (ask for 'Vernon') Direct Line —	071	199 3939

NAME	CODE	NUMBER
Certain Video Club → (free delivery in a pizza box)	071	989 4562
Chigwell Police Station — (Emergencies only!)		722 428

✳ <u>MY CONSULTANTS</u> ✳

Dr. Levy, my gynaecologist 071 870 1695
Mr Salamone, breast implants 071 531 7043
Denholm Judelson (dermatologist for 'HARD' skin) — 081 322 1194
Mr. Magi Yacoub — cellulite removal 071 455 6001

Tip Hanson — homeopath 081 892 8079

PETER MARR, Chiropractor
071 940 7915

Dr. Jacobson, for anything else

071 864 3996

© BAREFACTS DIARY 1994

NAME	CODE	NUMBER

Rocky, June '94

DATE	ITEM	TOTAL EXPENSES	RECEIPTS	BALANCE
	TOTAL			

FOR DORIEN GREEN'S EYES ONLY

PERSONAL EXPENSES

DATE	ITEM	TOTAL EXPENSES	RECEIPTS	BALANCE
	Harrods Sale - French Lingerie	544·00		CUTTIES:
	French deli home delivery - Gross of French sticks	75·00		
	Marks & Spencer	193·00		100·00
	Busybee dry-cleaners (persistent grass stains)	194·00		35·00
	COLOUR CONSULTATION	1904·00		30·00
	TOP SHOP - (REMEMBER TO CUT OUT THE LABELS)	50·00		2750·00
	KNICKER BOX	35·00		50·00
	IRONING SERVICE	£19·00		27·00
	MRS PEARSON	15·00		190·00
	TROY'S HOME MASSAGE (£20 TIP - WHAT A TROJAN HORSE)	48·00		
	150 PLANTS (MURDO SAYS I'VE GREEN FINGERS - I CAN MAKE ANYTHING GROW!)	579·00		
	HARRODS - FIORUCCI DRESS	2750·00		
	MR SALAMONE - consultation for breast enlargement + £200·00 (£100 each)			
	WAXING, FOR YOU	27·00		
	SCOTLAND: 2 × FLIGHTS, HOTELS, CAR HIRE, EXTRAS! £1430			
	Taxis	£190·00		
	TOTAL	£8203·00		

DATE	ITEM	TOTAL EXPENSES	RECEIPTS	BALANCE
	Mr Salamone consultation	300·00		
	Lagerfeld dress (½ square metre of material)	3500·00		
	Marks & Spencer - month's supply ready-cooked food	750·00		
	Harrods	72·50		
	Browns (nice of them to accept a cheque)	4854·00		
	French Deli deliveries	262·20		
	Janet Reger	322·60		
	Bubbles: Champagne delivery × 4 crates	5316·00		
	Boots The Chemist	800·00		
	Noskids Dry Cleaners	142·00		
	Tip Hanson, Homeopath (tipped me all night!!)	50·00		
	Southampton Holiday Inn - room, champagne etc, etc...	380·00		
	Mr Magi Yacoub consultation : cellulite removal	400·00		
	Taxis	375·00		
	Restaurants	790·00		
	TOTAL	£18,014·30		

FEBRUARY

NosKids Dry Cleaners

ITEM:
Joseph wool
suit.
Removal of
grass stains on
back of skirt and
jacket

TOTAL   £19.39
●116
VAT Included

S

DATE	ITEM			TOTAL EXPENSES	RECEIPTS	BALANCE
	BOLI JEWELLERS – valued M.'s watch (FAKE!!)			65·00		
	PARIS: flights, hotels, extras(!)			2500·00		
	Restaurant Marie Antoinette – £50 for a ticket & the soups cold !! F 3612			£9.99 – or is that Lire?		
	PREMIER COUTURE – £ 90999			£14320 – am I losing my touch?		
	CHANEL			£100·00		
	INTERFLORA (mummy's flowers)			?? – forgot to keep a record !!		
T	LE SKI CLOTHERS			£2500 –		
U	HOSPITAL BILLS			150·00		
2	French deli delivery – 2 gross french sticks –			53·00		
	Chauffering services (HUGHIE)					
4	Bar Mitzvah present (membership to Hurlingham AND £1000 cash)			£95·00		
W	Dr Jacobson: Injections for Indonesia			109·00		
	Taxis			£1900·00		
	Restaurants			????·??		
		TOTAL				
			TOTAL			

© BAREFACTS DIARY 1994

DATE	ITEM	TOTAL EXPENSES	RECEIPTS	BALANCE
	STAG SUITCASES - nice, smooth, buttery, sweaty leather!			£300.00
	INDONESIA: FLIGHT, HOTELS, MASSAGES	£2400.00		
	Rickshaw hire - cheaper to buy one - so, I did!	140.00		
	SILK WARDROBE	100.00		
	Pak Lok Cuk £170.00 per day & well worth it!!	1753.00		
	Dubai Duty Free	98.00		
	Vidal Sassoon	273.00		
	Taxis	£2000.00		
	Donation to Oxfam	£2000.00		
	Restaurants			
	TOTAL: AT LEAST £9744.00			

OXFAM

Thank you
for your generous
...

PERSONAL EXPENSES

DATE	ITEM		TOTAL EXPENSES	RECEIPTS	BALANCE
	CLINGFILM - worked well - kept him FRESH !!		50·00		
	Saturn Pharmacy - Vitamins E, C, B1, B6, Zinc, magnesium				£298·00
	Antigua: Flights, hotel, etc, etc.		£6037·00		
	Harrods - remember to return dress - soiled		£3010·00		
	SELFRIDGES		500·00		
	Tarot reading		£52·00		
X	Sotheby's Torture Catalogue - torture to resist anything			£45·00	
♉	Bar Mitzvah present - membership to thurlingham AND				
	£1250 cash		-£3900·00		
♏	SHARON - sponsored run to Brixton Prison 10p per mile				
			60P		
	Taxis		£516·00		
	Restaurants		£1913·00		
	Total (give or take the odd hairdo)		£16,321·60		
TOTAL					

© BAREFACTS DIARY 1994

DATE	ITEM	TOTAL EXPENSES	RECEIPTS	BALANCE
	Sven's Pressie - leather pouch to put his valuables in . £63·00			wow!
	Leather cat suit	280·00		maybe I want it twice?
	Rocky & Razor ... or was it Razor then Rocky? £50·00			wear it twice?!!
	Post House	£375·00		
(1)	Champagne Delivery - 1 x crate	579·00		
	Joseph ... Jesus & Mary !! The price!!	£6800·00 !!!!		
2	Dr Levy consultation	524·00		
1	...ductive evening for Marcus - what a waste - £475·00			
1	...ourt tickets to Wimbledon - (Close shave with Agassi)	£547·00		
		— £160·00		
		£3285·00		
	The Grand Total: £13,138·00			

DATE	ITEM	TOTAL EXPENSES	RECEIPTS	BALANCE
	New York: flights, hotels, extras	£4530·00		
	BLOOMINGDALES – WONDERFUL SERVICE!!	$20560 -sterling ??		
	Boodle & Oodles	7580·00		
	Alistair McCormack security consultation –£150–			
	Harrods facial testing – mumbled something about walnuts... £100–			
	Bill Myers – landscape gardening consultation 15·00			
	Window Cleaner. You've heard of window I can... £60–			
	knitting machine – move Tracey I think	£199·00		
	Motor mechanics course	£40-00		
	Photographers fee for retouching photos	£400-00		
	Taxis	£312-00		
	Restaurants	£532-00		
	Total :	~~~~~~		
	How many to the ?·?· ?	£13,918.00 +		
	dollars pound ?· ?	Bloomingdales		
	$20560			
	÷ or × ??			
	= £sterling			

TOTAL

© BAREFACTS DIARY 1994

DATE	ITEM				TOTAL EXPENSES	RECEIPTS	BALANCE
AUGUST	Wax Factor — ouch !!				23.00		
	Tennis club renewal (open new turf account)				800.00		
	Harrods — new tennis clothes				514.00		
	Larry — Interior Design — 1st payment				540.00		
	'Bubbles': 5 x bottles Pimms no. 5 @ £12.00 each						
	(with Larry's friend, Pym)				60.00		
	SARDINIA: flights, hotels, extras: £4600						
	Taxis				512.00		
	Charity event with Tracey (for HANDCUFFS, ex-prisoners						
	association)				120.00		
	Tickets to Sunset Boulevard				60.00		
	Restaurants				800.00		
	ᴛᴏᴛAUGUST TOTAL :				£ 8,029.00		Cheap month — is that ALL?

DATE	ITEM	TOTAL EXPENSES	RECEIPTS	BALANCE
	Book shop - bought Freud's Interpretation of Dreams - been having some interesting ones lately... and some other worthy books -	79.00	The best	
	Shaggers Hair Salon	70.00	sprog for now but weeks!!	
	Red Herring Caterers	£600.00		
	Mandy's Wine Bar (RANDY Mandy!!)	245.00		
	Restaurants	£460.00		
	Taxis	£83.00		
	Video Hire	2.50 +		
	+ extra £25.00 to delivery boy for showing me how to work the machine	25.00		
	Zulu Warriors hire	100.00 each		
	2 months subscription - Weight Watchers - £100.00 - (Sharon of course).	100.00		
	School Uniform	320.00 - GOOD! can still get my size...!		
	TOTAL:	who cares!!		

September

TOTAL

© BAREFACTS DIARY 1994

DATE	ITEM	TOTAL EXPENSES	RECEIPTS	BALANCE
	TAXIS	370·00		
	Window Cleaner – bought new squeezy....!	93·00		
	THE LOG CHALET & SAUNA COMPANY, consultation	300·00 – some		
	mistake....! I thought THEY were paying ME ??			
	WH Smiths for typewriter ribbon	5·00 – it left		
	a black mark on my forehead....!			
Oct 06 en	Flowers for Melanie (what came over me??)	£50·00		
	French deli delivery – 150 french sticks	40·00		
	Donation to Conservative Party	£2000·00		
	Birthday present for ME! – 1 crate champagne	270·00		
	– 2kgs best Beluga	175·00		
	– 3 of Ann Summer's			
	latest toys......	£73·50		
	TOTAL	£3043·50		

WARNING
THIS TOY IS NOT
SUITABLE FOR
ANYONE UNDER THE
AGE OF 18

TOTAL

DATE	ITEM	TOTAL EXPENSES	RECEIPTS	BALANCE
~~	Bus Fare	20.00 – no change for note.		
↘	Wax Factor (no pain, no gain!)	£27.50		
	Lunch with Kelvin	108.00		⎱ needed the
	Dinner with Kelvin	310.00		⎰ calories!
☰	Breakfast with Kelvin	35.00		
∞	French Deli – emergency supplies	70.00		
	Phone bill	630.00		
∽	Video hire	30.00		
W	Restaurants	163.00 – terrible month for entertaining		
N O V E				
~~	Taxis	£45.00		
	anyone would think I was saving for Christmas!	TOTAL –£1438.50		

BAREFACTS DIARY 1994

DATE	ITEM	TOTAL EXPENSES	RECEIPTS	BALANCE
🎄	Sole Mio Restaurant, Venice - what a romantic evening - shame Marcus was ill in bed — L437000			
	Francesca's - Italian salesmen are so persuasive — L9780000			
🎄	Dino's L64300 ??			
🎄	Harrods - Christmas shopping (always do everything there.) — £4000·00			
🎄	Fortnum's Christmas & New Year Survival Hamper ... £ 875·00			
🎄	Woolworth's - last minute shopping for Marcus's relatives £63·00			
🎄	Browns a few outfits for Christmas - £5300·00			
	Restaurants £607000			
	Taxis 594·00			
🎄	TOTAL £16,902 (ex Lira)			The festive season !!
	ANNUAL TOTAL — MUST be less than last year?			

The GOLD Card

Statement of Account

DORIEN GREEN
BRYAN CLOSE
CHIGWELL
ESSEX
CM 12

Please Quote Your Gold
Card Number in all
Correspondence

1004 753 543 196

Statement Date

05/10/94

REF: 21763M

Date Received by us	Reference Number	Description	Previous Balance
			8035.25
		PAYMENT RECEIVED - THANK YOU *well done Marcus*	⟋ 8000.00
01/09/94	025317	PAMPER DELUXE HEALTH FARM	4534.05
02/09/94	131744	BUSYBEES DRY CLEANING	250.00
04/09/94	146231	PETROL SUNNINGDALE SERVICES	30.00
04/09/9	213119	SUNNINGDALE MERCEDES	240.00

D A

© BAREFACTS DIARY 1994

DATE	ITEM		TOTAL EXPENSES	RECEIPTS	BALANCE
06/09/94	440037	BROWNS, SOUTH MOLTON STREET		1500.00	
		A girl needs cheering up after a car crash			
.0/09/94	541035	HARRODS		2999.99	
11/09/94	629399	MARKS AND SPENCER		14.99	
15/09/94	461801	F W WOOLWORTHS - *Mrs Pearsons*		3.50	
		birthday - saw a lovely t-shirt in the sale.			
15/09/94	562310	KURT RHEINGOLD ASSOCIATES		1000.00	
18/09/94	414923	SELFRIDGES - *catering pack of*		1300.00	
		Manhunter perfume			
21/09/94	311214	THE POST HOUSE		235.00	
		Standing Double room reservation			
			New Balance	£ 13142.78	

DETACH HERE AND RETAIN STATEMENT

DONT FORGET – YOU WILL GET 20 AIR MILES FOR EVERY £500 SPENT WITH YOUR GOLD CARD

TOTAL

AD97

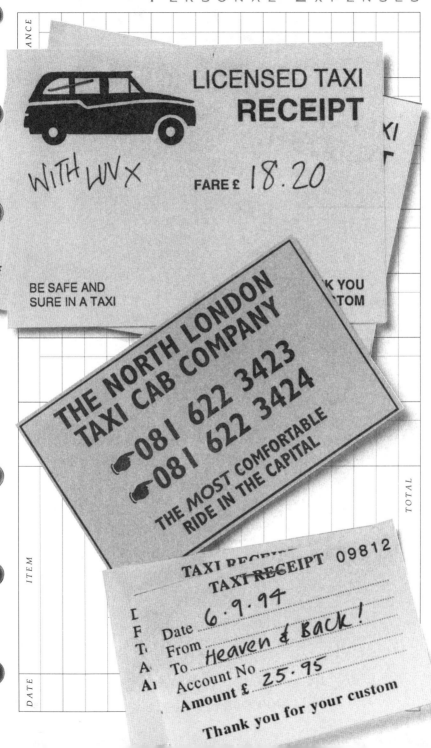

© BAREFACTS DIARY

LICENSED TAXI
RECEIPT

WITH LUV X

FARE £ 18.20

BE SAFE AND
SURE IN A TAXI

THE NORTH LONDON
TAXI CAB COMPANY
☎ 081 622 3423
☎ 081 622 3424
THE MOST COMFORTABLE
RIDE IN THE CAPITAL

TAXI RECEIPT 09812
Date 6.9.94
From Heaven & Back !
To
Account No
Amount £ 25.95
Thank you for your custom

BROGANS
BRASSERIE

13 Gabri

4 x
2 x 1
2 x
2 J
Me

St. Pierre Restaurant

214 Barkley Mews, London
Telephone 081 456 9123

La Capallina

R I S T O R A N T E

Thank you for dining at La Capallina. Your
meal is itemized as follows:

2 x Prawn Remoulade	£18.50
2 x Marinated Trout Florentine	£65.00
2 x La Capallina Love Truffles	£30.00
2 x Bottle of Chablis	£70.00
Total	£183.50

We hope you enjoyed your time with us and we
look forward to repeating this pleasure

17 St. Matthews Gardens, London.
Telephone 071 009 9963

.00

50.00

£24.00

£120.00

£215.00

BALANCE

RECEIPTS

TOTAL EXPENSES

HARVEY NICHOLS

Black Leather Jodphurs
Leopard Skin Jacket
Front-zipped Lycra Bodysuit
Horse Whip

Total £630.00

GUCCI

Purchase Receipt

Classic Cut Cashmere
suit in Fuschia

White Silk blouse with

pearl buttons

Total Price £1250.00

call

CHANEL
RECEIPT

GOLD LAMÉ SEQUINED
VEST WITH MATCHING
MICRO SKIRT.

TOTAL £850.00

ur custom

THANK YOU FOR VISITING
OUR SALON

TOTAL

ITEM

DATE

THE HONEY TREE HEALTH FARM

HONEY TREE LANE
MORETON-IN-THE-MARSH
GLOUCESTERSHIRE
GL19 4HF
TELEPHONE: 0981 359
FAX: 0981 658

INVOICE No. 52130

Dorien Green
Bryan Close
Chigwell
Essex
CM12

2 Nights de luxe suite @ £250
(Including Half Board)

Aroma rapy   £5
2 Sess ns @ £25

8 Sessions @ £25
(all with Kurt by request)   £200

Private hire of jacuzzi for 1 night   £300

Extras: Baby Oil - 10 litres @ £3.50   £35
Condoms - 2 dozen @ 50p   £12

Phonecalls from husband dealt with
3 @ £50   £150

SUB-TOTAL   £1247.00
VAT @ 17.5%   £187.05
TOTAL   £1434.05

Thank you for calling and please come again soon

DATE	ITEM	TOTAL EXPENSES	RECEIPTS	BALANCE

TOTAL

DATE	NAME	AGE	CARD	GIFT
26.2	Melanie Fishman — (must remember to forget it)			
5.3	MUMMY (standing order of white lilies in sympathy)	73	✓	✓
31.3	Marcus's Auntie Sadie REMEMBER — she's on her last legs!			✓
14.5	Marcus's Uncle Harry — DITTO			
15.6	MARCUS	?	✓	✓
26.6	FATHER			
30.9	Sharon	not as old as she looks!		✓
	Star Sign — LIBRA			
27.10	*My birthday* — SCORPIO			
19.12	Tracey Star Sign: SAGITTARIUS	?	✓	✓
				I suppose so!

BOOKS I'VE READ THIS YEAR

* The Importance of Being Earnest-
  Oscar Wilde (only read ½)

* In Praise of Panty Hose -
  Sabina Sedgewick (wow!)

* My Secret Garden - Nancy Friday
  (must try some out!)

* Herbs for Youthful Skin-Crescent
  Smith

* Facial Workout -Colin Sears

* The Cellulite War - Dr. James Honey

* Healthy, Wealthy & Wise - A
  Guide to Success - Myra Browning,
  MBA, PhD, ETA

* The Joy of Eternal Youth... and
  how to achieve it - Alaison
  Mary Reynolda.

* CARS THAT ARE <u>GOOD</u> TO
DO IT IN :

1. Rolls 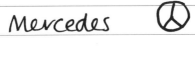 ✓

2. Jag ✓

3. <u>BIG</u> Mercedes ✓

* CARS THAT ARE <u>BAD</u> TO
DO IT IN:

1. <u>All</u> reps cars with hangers
on the grab handle. ✗

✗ 2. Marcus's car (how to explain
away heel marks on roof lining?)

3. cars with alarms that go
off if they rock too hard!! ✗

You are invited to the

exclusive preview

of

THE NEW COLLECTION
OF BARELY THERE SWIMWEAR

4th May - 7.30 pm

277 South Melton Street, London.

Wine & a light buffet will be served

B.T.E

They're stunning -
Almost indecent !

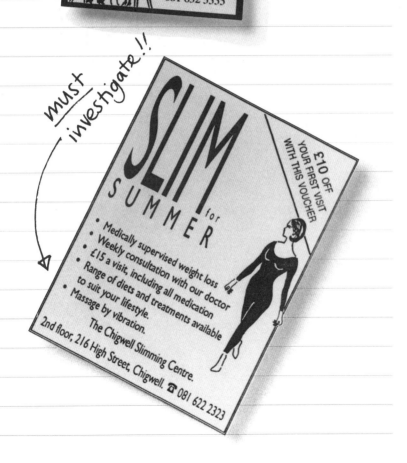

DEAR DORIEN,

SAW YOUR CAR - HAVEN'T SEEN
YOU FOR A WHILE - SURE YOU'VE BEEN BUSY - WE
OUGHT TO GET TOGETHER AGAIN SOMETIME......
CHELMSFORD FOOTBALL TEAM

Milkman
2 pints of
cream please
X

ON DAIRI
INDUSTRIAL

Milk is good for you

X

I'm getting low
a bit but but I'll
do my best!

© BAREFACTS DIARY 1994

only six roses - still, it's the thought that counts.

To my Valentine

x x x

Was this from Simon??

With Love to my Valentine

EXCLUSIVE LINGERIE BY POST

Mare Sainer
AGONY AUNT

Monday 9th May 1994

Dear Doris of Chigwell,

I found your letter fascinating, but far too outré to print in the delicate columns of the Sunday Sport. Your sort of condition is not rare, but be re-assured, you are not a nymphomaniac. Nymphomania is a morbid condition and sufferers do not actually enjoy sex. Not your problem I fear.

It seems to me your main hang-up is simply classic Jewish guilt vis à vis hubbie and mum. And why not? you're a size ten, rich,gorgeous, and you get laid 15 times a week. You want to feel good too? Okay, I admit it, I'm jealous.

Keep taking the precautions.

Mare.

Thank <u>GOD</u>
for that !!

I'm normal!

(shame she couldn't
publish.)

Found this fascinating
old print in 'Astro Monthly'.

Gemini:
no wonder
M. has
big...
shoulders.

Scorpio-
what an
INTERESTING
part of the
body to
be associated
to !!

Melanie 'fishfeet' Fishman.

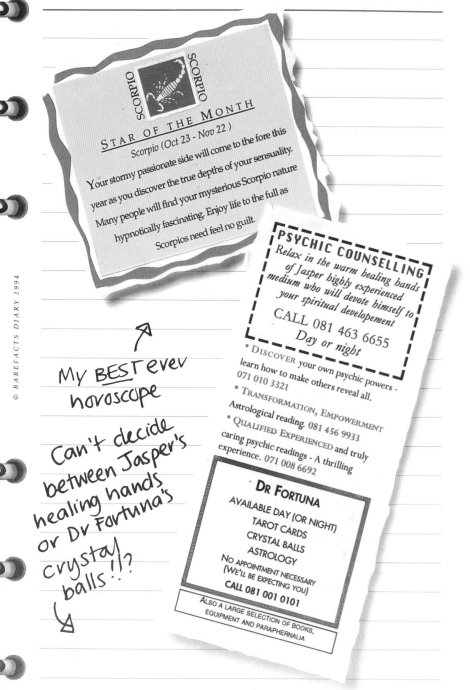

SCORPIO SCORPIO

STAR OF THE MONTH

Scorpio (Oct 23 - Nov 22)

Your stormy passionate side will come to the fore this year as you discover the true depths of your sensuality. Many people will find your mysterious Scorpio nature hypnotically fascinating. Enjoy life to the full as Scorpios need feel no guilt.

My BEST ever horoscope

Can't decide between Jasper's healing hands or Dr Fortuna's crystal balls !!?

PSYCHIC COUNSELLING

Relax in the warm healing hands of Jasper highly experienced medium who will devote himself to your spiritual developement

CALL 081 463 6655
Day or night

- DISCOVER your own psychic powers - learn how to make others reveal all. 071 010 3321

- TRANSFORMATION, EMPOWERMENT Astrological reading. 081 456 9933

- QUALIFIED EXPERIENCED and truly caring psychic readings - A thrilling experience. 071 008 6692

DR FORTUNA

AVAILABLE DAY (OR NIGHT)
TAROT CARDS
CRYSTAL BALLS
ASTROLOGY

NO APPOINTMENT NECESSARY
(WE'LL BE EXPECTING YOU)

CALL 081 001 0101

ALSO A LARGE SELECTION OF BOOKS, EQUIPMENT AND PARAPHERNALIA

IDEAS FOR MY <u>EXCLUSIVE</u> KNITWEAR RANGE

<u>BIKINI</u>

cone shaped

'G' string bottom

fantastic range of colours

sent off for these scrummy yarns

EVENING

Great in
pink &
turquoise

turquoise with
silver sequins??

* <u>MUST</u> find an exciting, talented,
(preferably male) designer to do
my tags for me

EXCLUSIVE

Dorien

DESIGNS

DESIGNED BY

Dorien

Perhaps it would be
easier to commission
someone else to make
my designs —
Tracey??

© DORIEN

PAVILION

26 UPPER GROUND
LONDON SE1 9PD
TELEPHONE 071-620 1666

FACSIMILE 071-620 1314

A delight! indeed!

1st July 199

Dorien Green
Bryan Close
Chigwell
Essex CM12

What a delight it was visiting you last week to discuss publishing possibilities for your manuscript indulgence. I confess had I known the meeting was there so inform me would have brought a coat-hanger. It was very kind of you to show me over the house and garden and let me see your holiday snaps. Please accept my sympathies about your husband Marcus. His breakdown must have been a great trial to you.

To your book. I have now had time to read the manuscript thoroughly and although it has great potential I'm afraid the prevailing economic climate makes new novelists difficult to establish. I am very much afraid therefore, I am unable offer you any publishing proposals at the present time. Please do keep in touch.

All best wishes.

Yours sincerely

Trevor Dolby
EDITORIAL DIRECTOR

July 8th 1997

Dear Mrs Green

Your visit to Pavilion's offices was rather startling. The pictures were, as was obvious, a bit of a shock. Believe me it had not occurred to me for one moment that I was ruining your life and that I had taken advantage of you. I would also suggest that any newspaper editor worth his salt would notice immediately that my head had been pasted onto the naked body of William Baldwin and your face onto Sharon Stone's. Please be aware that I᾿m not susceptible to blackmail.

Yours sincerely

Trevor Dolby
EDITORIAL DIRECTOR

PAVILION
26 UPPER GROUND
LONDON SE1 9PD
TELEPHONE 071-620 1666
FACSIMILE 071-620 1314

Dorien Green
Bryan Close
Chigwell
Essex CM12

15th July 1994 *yippee!!*

Dear Mrs Green

I confess the letter from Kelvin McKenzie was unexpected. Under the circumstances I would be delighted to publish you novel.

good old kelvin!

Yours sincerely

Trevor Dolby
EDITORIAL DIRECTOR

You are invited to
The Royal Charity Premier Performance
of
'CONFUSION'
the new film directed by
BRAD CONWAY
in the company of
HRH PRINCE EDWARD
at the Empire Cinema Leicester Square

<u>ACKNOWLEDGEMENTS</u>

The publishers would like to thank:

Carole Bennett, Dash (tennis gear),
Troy Halliday, Helen Holmes, Suzie
Hooper, Kerry Ann Hurst, Herbert Johnson
(Dorien's hat and hat boxes), Stephen
Keane, Lillywhites (tennis gear), Francis
Loney, Sandy McCullough, Claire McGee,
Kelley-Anne McGee, Helen Mitchell, Vivien
Placks, Scott Robinson, Keith Saunders,
Linda Siefert, Jeremy Thomas.

THE END